**1 YEAR**

Classworks
# Numeracy

## Series editors

Len and Anne Frobisher

## Author team

**Len Frobisher, Anne Frobisher**

John Taylor, John Spooner, Thelma Page

Published in 2003 by:
Nelson Thornes Ltd
Delta Place
27 Bath Road
CHELTENHAM
GL53 7TH
United Kingdom

03 04 05 06 07 / 10 9 8 7 6 5 4 3 2 1

A catalogue record for this book is available from the British Library

ISBN 0 7487 7335 5

Illustrations by Tim Oliver
Page make-up by Hart McLeod
Cover photograph © Corbis EI 170 (NT)

Printed in Great Britain by Ashford Colour Press

**CLASSWORKS – BLUEPRINTS – LEARNING TARGETS – LASTMINUTELESSON.CO.UK**

Nelson Thornes publishes teacher's resource books packed with flexible ideas for use in primary schools. As well as *Classworks*,
Nelson Thornes publishes *Blueprints* and *Learning Targets*, providing busy teachers with unbeatable curriculum coverage, inspiration
and value for money. We mail teachers and schools about new Nelson Thornes publications regularly. To join the mailing list simply
photocopy and complete the form below and return using the FREEPOST address to receive regular updates on our new and existing
titles. Books can be bought by credit card over the telephone or Internet. For more details log on to www.nelsonthornes.com or contact
us on 01242 267 280.
For FREE resources register at www.lastminutelesson.co.uk

Please add my name to the Nelson Thornes Teacher's Resources mailing list.

Mr/Mrs/Miss/Ms _____

Address _____
_____
_____

Postcode _____

School address _____
_____
_____

Postcode _____

To: Direct Marketing Coordinator, Nelson Thornes Ltd, FREEPOST SWC 0507,
Cheltenham GL53 7ZZ

# *Contents*

# *Introduction*

## How *Classworks* works

**What this book contains**

- Visual resources for structuring mental, written and problem-solving work.
- Examples of modelled mathematical methods and solutions.
- Lesson ideas including key questions and plenary support.
- Photocopiable pages to aid and structure pupil work.
- Blocked units to slot into medium-term planning.
- Oral/mental starter ideas to complement the daily teaching of mental facts and skills.
- Every idea is brief, to the point, and on one page.

**How this book is organised**

- There are blocked units of work from one week to several, depending on the strand.
- Each blocked unit is organised into a series of chunks of teaching content.
- Each 'chunk' has accompanying suggestions for visual modelling of teaching.
- For many teaching ideas we supply photocopiable resources.
- The objectives covered in the units are based on DfES sample medium-term planning.
- The units are organised in strand-based chunks, in a suggested order for teaching.

## Planning a unit of work

**How to incorporate *Classworks* material into your medium-term plan**

- Pick the most relevant unit for what you want to teach – the units are organised in strands, sequentially according to the DfES sample medium-term plans.
- To find the content, look at the objectives on the first page of every unit.
- Or just browse through by topic, picking out the ideas you want to adapt.
- Every page has its content clearly signalled so you can pick and choose.
- Choose a generic starter from the bank at the back of the book if required.

# *What each page does*

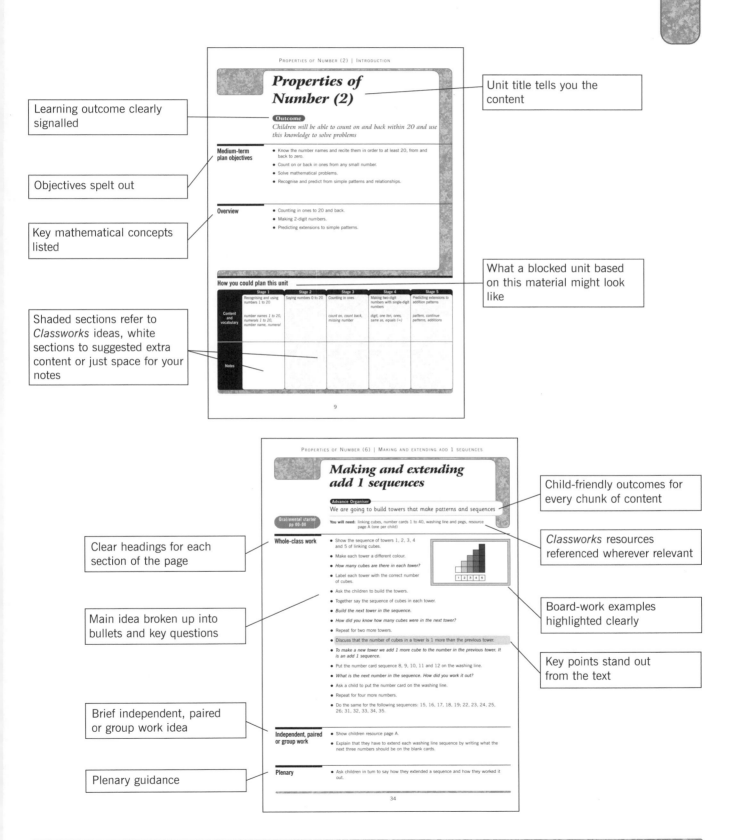

Unit title tells you the content

Learning outcome clearly signalled

Objectives spelt out

Key mathematical concepts listed

Shaded sections refer to *Classworks* ideas, white sections to suggested extra content or just space for your notes

What a blocked unit based on this material might look like

Child-friendly outcomes for every chunk of content

*Classworks* resources referenced wherever relevant

Clear headings for each section of the page

Board-work examples highlighted clearly

Main idea broken up into bullets and key questions

Key points stand out from the text

Brief independent, paired or group work idea

Plenary guidance

# Properties of Number (1)

## Outcome

*Children can count a set of objects and write one more*

**Medium-term plan objectives**

- Know the number names and recite them in order to at least 20.
- Count reliably at least 20 objects.
- Count on in ones from any small number.
- Read numerals from 1 to at least 20.
- Write numerals from 1 to 10.
- Say the number that is one more or less than a given number to 20.
- Begin to know what each digit in a two-digit number represents.
- Partition a 'teens' number into tens and ones.

**Overview**

- Counting to 20 and writing the matching numeral.
- Predicting one more.
- Predicting one less.
- Making a number into tens and ones.

## How you could plan this unit

| | Stage 1 | Stage 2 | Stage 3 | Stage 4 | Stage 5 |
|---|---|---|---|---|---|
| **Content and vocabulary** | Count at least 20 objects and write numerals<br><br>*count, how many* | Predict and work out the number that is one more<br><br>*good guess, predict, add, add one, one more than, hidden number* | Predict and work out the number that is one less<br><br>*good guess, predict, take away, one less than, fewer* | Make a set of linking cubes into one 10-stick and ones<br><br>*ten-stick, one ten, ones, same as, equals (=)* | |
| **Notes** | Resource page A | Resource page B | Resource page C | | |

# Count at least 20 objects and write numerals

**Advance Organiser**

We are going to count objects and write how many

**Oral/mental starter p 181**

**You will need:** a variety of objects, a hoop, 1 to 20 number cards, resource page A (one per child and one enlarged), counters, cubes or other objects

## Whole-class work

- Sit children around you. Put seven counters in a line in the hoop.

- Ask a child: *Count how many counters are in the hoop.*

- Show how to count by touching an object in turn and giving it its number name.

- Add the number card seven to the hoop.

- Have other children count how many counters. Start counting from different counters.

- *Why is the answer always seven?*

- Repeat with other objects increasing the number up to 20.

- Repeat the activity with objects randomly positioned in the hoop.

- *Is it easier to count correctly when the counters are in a straight line? Why do you find that?*

- Repeat with other objects and larger numbers, moving objects around and re-counting them to prove that the number of objects stays the same no matter how they are arranged.

- Have an enlarged copy of resource page A to show the children.

- Demonstrate the activity, counting the sheep and marking each one as you do so, then writing the appropriate number on the sheet.

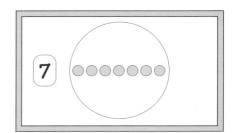

## Independent, paired or group work

- One child counts out a number of counters greater than 10. Their partner checks the number.

- Roles are reversed. They repeat until told to stop.

- Each child in a pair works on resource page A.

- After each question they compare answers and do not move on until they agree how many.

## Plenary

- Using counters, repeat counting a number of objects in a straight line.

- Reposition the objects in a random order and count again to demonstrate that there are the same number. Repeat.

- End with counting together from 1 to 20 and back again.

**PUPIL PAGE**

Name: _____

# How many?

| | |
|---|---|
| | There are ⬡ sheep |
| | There are ⬡ planes |
| | There are ⬡ monkeys |
| | There are ⬡ goats |
| | There are ⬡ bees |
| | There are ⬡ cars |
| | There are ⬡ geese |

*Classworks* © Classworks Numeracy author team, Nelson Thornes Ltd, 2003

# Predict and work out the number that is one more

**Advance Organiser**

We are going to find out what one more means

Oral/mental starter
p 181

**You will need:** a variety of objects, a hoop, a cloth to cover the hoop, a bag, 1 to 20 number cards, resource page B (one per child and one enlarged)

## Whole-class work

- Put five randomly placed counters in the hoop.
- *I want you to look carefully at how many counters there are.*
- Cover the counters.
- *Show me the card that shows how many counters are in the hoop.*
- Remove the cover. Together count how many.
- Put another counter in the hoop saying: *I am putting in one more.* Cover the counters.
- *Show me the card that says how many counters are in the hoop now.*
- Tell them that they have made a good guess and that we call this a prediction.
- Ask different children how they decided what their good guess (prediction) was.
- *Let us check how many are in the hoop.* Remove the cover and together count how many.
- Say and ask the children to repeat: *1 more than 5 counters is 6 counters. 1 more than 5 is 6.*
- Repeat the exercise with cubes in a bag, counting out the cubes one by one to check.
- Show the children an enlarged copy of resource page B.
- Read together what is below the picture explaining that each cloud is hiding a number.
- Point to the first cloud. *What number is hidden under this cloud?* Write the number in the cloud.
- Repeat for the second number. Together read out the completed sentence.

## Independent, paired or group work

- Each child works on resource page B.

## Plenary

- Use the enlarged resource page B. Point to an example and ask a child to tell everyone about the picture and what the hidden numbers are. Repeat with the other examples.
- Ask questions such as: *What is 1 more than 2?*
- End with you saying a number and the children holding up the number that is one more than your number.

Name: _____

# 1 more than

| | |
|---|---|
| | 4 ducks and 1 more duck<br><br>is (  ) ducks |
| | 6 birds and 1 more bird<br><br>is (  ) birds |
| | 5 cows and 1 more cow<br><br>is (  ) cows |
| | 3 horses and 1 more horse<br><br>is (  ) horses |
| | (  ) dogs and 1 more dog<br><br>is (  ) dogs |
| | (  ) cats and (  ) more cat<br><br>is (  ) cats |

# Predict and work out the number that is one less

**Advance Organiser**

We are going to find out what one less means

Oral/mental starter p 181

**You will need:** a variety of objects, a hoop, a cloth to cover the hoop, a bag, 1 to 20 number cards, resource page C (one per child and one enlarged)

## Whole-class work

- Put three randomly placed counters in the hoop.
- *Show me the card that shows how many counters are in the hoop.*
- Put the 3 number card in the hoop.
- Take a counter out of the hoop saying: *I am taking out one counter.*
- *Show me the card that says how many counters are in the hoop now.*
- Replace the 3 card with the 2 card saying: *1 less than 3 counters is 2 counters, 1 less than 3 is 2.*
- Repeat using cubes in a bag.
- Say and write on the board: *5 cubes and 1 less cube is 4 cubes. 5 and 1 less is 4. 1 less than 5 cubes is 4 cubes. 1 less than 5 is 4.*
- Ask the children to read with your help what is on the board.
- Repeat with different objects and numbers up to 10.
- Show the children an A3 size copy of resource page C.
- Point to the first picture. Tell them a story of the picture using 'one less'.
- Read together what is below the picture explaining that each cloud is hiding a number.
- Demonstrate completing an activity.

> 5 and 1 less is 4
>
> 1 less than 5 is 4

## Independent, paired or group work

- Each child works on resource page C.

## Plenary

- Use the A3 size resource page C. Point to an example and ask a child to tell everyone about the picture and what the hidden numbers are. Repeat with the other examples.
- Ask questions such as: *What is 1 less than 3?*
- End with you saying a number and the children holding up the number that is one less than your number.

Name: _____

# 1 less than

| | |
|---|---|
| | 5 ducks less 1 duck is ⬭ |
| | 1 less than 5 is ⬭ |
| | 7 apples less 1 apple is ⬭ |
| | 1 less than 7 is ⬭ |
| | ⬭ frogs less 1 frog is ⬭ |
| | 1 less than ⬭ is ⬭ |
| | ⬭ eggs less 1 egg is ⬭ |
| | 1 less than ⬭ is ⬭ |
| | ⬭ birds less 1 bird is ⬭ |
| | 1 less than ⬭ is ⬭ |

# Make a set of linking cubes into one 10-stick and ones

**Oral/mental starter
p 181**

**Advance Organiser**

We are going to make a ten-stick using linking cubes

**You will need:** linking cubes, 1 to 20 number cards

**Whole-class work**

- Put 11 linking cubes in a hoop.
- Together, count how many cubes there are. Put the 11 number card in the hoop.
- Ask two children to each give you a cube.
- Link the two cubes together.
- *How many cubes in this stick?*
- Repeat until you have a 10-stick.
- Together, everyone counts the number of cubes in the stick. *This is a 10-stick.*
- Put the 10-stick into the hoop with the single extra cube.
- *Hold up a number card to show me how many cubes there are in the hoop.*
- Ask some children to explain how they know there are still 11.
- Together, count the cubes starting with the ones in the 10-stick.
- Write and say: *10 and 1 make 11. 11 is the same as 10 and 1.*
- Read together what you have written.
- Repeat for different numbers, making sticks of 10 and sticks of 2, 3, 4 and so on.

**Independent, paired or group work**

- Children repeat the above steps with cubes numbering up to 19, writing down: *14 is the same as 10 and 4. 10 and 4 make 14*, and so on.
- Above average achievers could look at writing the sum of 10 and ones in equivalent ways: *10 + 9 = 19, 19 = 10 + 9; 10 + 8 = 18, 18 = 10 + 8* and so on. It helps children if the 'equals sign' is read as 'is the same as'.

**Plenary**

- Invite the children to show how they would use cubes to find the missing number in a fact such as 10 + □ = 16.
- With the help of the children build on the board the pattern from 11 to 19 shown here.
- Cover up numbers in the table and ask the children which you have covered.
- End with holding up, for example, a 10-stick and a 3-stick, asking how many cubes there are altogether.

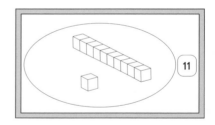

| | |
|---|---|
| 11 = 10 + 1 | 16 = 10 + 6 |
| 12 = 10 + 2 | 17 = 10 + 7 |
| 13 = 10 + 3 | 18 = 10 + 8 |
| 14 = 10 + 4 | 19 = 10 + 9 |
| 15 = 10 + 5 | |

# Properties of Number (2)

**Outcome**

*Children will be able to count on and back within 20 and use this knowledge to solve problems*

**Medium-term plan objectives**

- Know the number names and recite them in order to at least 20, from and back to zero.
- Count on or back in ones from any small number.
- Solve mathematical problems.
- Recognise and predict from simple patterns and relationships.

**Overview**

- Counting in ones to 20 and back.
- Making 2-digit numbers.
- Predicting extensions to simple patterns.

## How you could plan this unit

| | Stage 1 | Stage 2 | Stage 3 | Stage 4 | Stage 5 |
|---|---|---|---|---|---|
| **Content and vocabulary** | Recognising and using numbers 1 to 20<br><br>*number names 1 to 20, numerals 1 to 20, number name, numeral* | Saying numbers 0 to 20 | Counting in ones<br><br>*count on, count back, missing number* | Making two-digit numbers with single-digit number cards<br><br>*digit, one ten, ones, same as, equals (=)* | Predicting extensions to addition patterns<br><br>*pattern, continue patterns, additions* |
| **Notes** | | | | | |

# Saying numbers 0 to 20

**Advance Organiser**

We are going to say the numbers 0 to 20 in order

**Oral/mental starter p 181**

**You will need:** 0 to 20 number cards, washing line and pegs, 0 to 20 number cards per pair, a blank number track with 21 empty boxes per pair

## Whole-class work

- Have the numbers 0 to 20 on a washing line in order with 0 on the children's left.
- *Say the numbers as I point to them.*
- Use a blank card to cover up a few of the numbers and repeat counting from 0 to 20.
- Repeat the activity covering more and more of the numbers.
- Point to the numbers in order, but starting with 20 and moving down to 0.

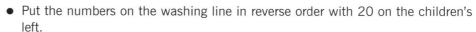

- Put the numbers on the washing line in reverse order with 20 on the children's left.
- Repeat the earlier activities that were used for 0 to 20.
- *Put your hands over your eyes.*
- Remove a number from the washing line.
- Children open their eyes.
- *Which number is missing?*
- Repeat the activity removing two or more cards.

## Independent, paired or group work

- Give each pair a set of 0 to 20 number cards placed face down.
- In turn, the children turn over a card until they find 0, turning each other card face down.
- They place 0 on the left of a number track.
- They repeat this finding the rest of the numbers 1 to 20 in order until the track is complete.
- One of the pair interchanges two of the numbers on the track secretly.
- Their partner has to identify the two switched numbers.
- This can be extended to three or more numbers.

## Plenary

- Randomly hold up one number card from 0 to 20.
- Together, the children say the number and all the numbers from the one shown up to 20 in order.
- Repeat the activity, but this time the children say the number and all the numbers in order down to 0.
- *Lift off!*

# *Counting in ones*

**Advance Organiser**

We are going to count in ones

Oral/mental starter
p 181

**You will need:** 1 to 30 number cards for you and per pair of children

## Whole-class work

- Together, the class count on in ones starting at 1 up to a number of your choosing.

- Have number cards 1 to 15 and 16 to 30 in two sets, both in a random order and face down.

- Choose two children: one takes a card from 1 to 15, the other one from 16 to 30 at random.

- The class count on starting at the smaller number and ending at the larger number.

- Repeat the activity counting back from the larger to the smaller.

- Give each pair a set of 1 to 30 number cards.

- *I am going to count from 1 to 30 but miss out a number.*

- *Find the card that has the number I missed out.*

- Extend the activity to missing out two or three numbers.

- Repeat the activity counting back from 30.

- Count silently from any number and tell the children the number you finish on.

- *Can you show me the card for my number?*

- *Can you show me the next number if I counted on one more?*

- Repeat the activity, but this time count back.

- *Can you show me the next number if I counted back one more?*

## Independent, paired or group work

- Children work in groups.

- One child counts on in ones silently from 1 and tells the group the number they finish at.

- The rest of the group have to say the next number that would be said.

- Children take turns to count on.

- Each group repeats the activity, but this time counts back in ones starting at 30.

## Plenary

- Say any number between 1 and 30.

- Each child holds up the next number they would say if they counted on from your number.

- For example, you say 15 and children hold up 16.

- Repeat the activity, but this time children say the number that is one before your number.

# Making two-digit numbers with single-digit number cards

**Advance Organiser**

We are going to solve some mathematical problems

**Oral/mental starter p 181**

**You will need:** 0 to 9 number cards, 1 to 100 number grid (enlarged), 1 to 30 number grid (one per pair), tens and units place value grid (one per pair)

## Whole-class work

- Make the number 24 with the 2 and 4 cards. Explain to the children that the 2 and 4 are digits.
- *What number have I made with these digits?*
- Ask for the value of the 2 and the 4.
- Together, look for the number 24 on the 1 to 100 grid.
- *What number will I get when I change over the 2 and the 4?*
- Show them the number.
- *What is the value of the 4? What is the value of the 2?*
- Together, look for the number on the 1 to 100 grid.
- Show the digits 1, 3, 4 and 7. Put the 1 in the tens position on a place value grid on the board.
- *Tell me the number I will make when I put the 3 in the units place.*
- Ask them where it is on the 1 to 100 grid.
- Make and record the number on the board. Do the same for the 4 and the 7.
- *How many different numbers have we made using the 3, the 4 or the 7 in the units place?*
- Together look for the numbers on the 1 to 100 grid.

| Tens | Units | |
|------|-------|----|
| 1 | 3 | 13 |
| 1 | 4 | 14 |
| 1 | 7 | 17 |

## Independent, paired or group work

- Children work in pairs with 1 to 3 number cards, a 1 to 30 number grid, a place value grid and a sheet of A4 paper.
- *Predict (make a good guess) how many different two-digit numbers you make using any two of the three digits.*
- *Write your prediction on your sheet: I predict that I can make ☐ numbers.*
- *Write each number you make on your sheet. Colour each number on your 1 to 30 number grid.*

## Plenary

- Ask the children what their predictions were and how many numbers they made.
- Invite a child to make a two-digit number with any two of the 0 to 9 cards.
- Ask them to tell you their number, the value of each digit and to point out the number on the 1 to 100 number grid.
- Write the number on the board and do not use those cards again.
- Repeat until all ten cards are used.

# Predicting extensions to addition patterns

**Advance Organiser**

We are going to investigate addition patterns

Oral/mental starter
p 181

**You will need:** prepared sheet of addition patterns (one per child; see below)

## Whole-class work

- Write on the board this sequence of additions.

- *What is the answer to 1 + 1?*

- Write in the answer and repeat for the other additions.

- Talk about the additions with the children.

- Draw their attention to the patterns in the additions.

- If necessary, say the additions developing a rhythm to bring out the patterns.

- Draw two incomplete additions below the others.

- *What numbers should I write in the boxes to continue the pattern?*

- Complete the addition.

- Repeat for two more lines.

$$1 + 1 =$$
$$2 + 2 =$$
$$3 + 3 =$$
$$4 + 4 =$$

## Independent, paired or group work

- Each child completes the additions below on your prepared sheet and extends the patterns for two more lines.

| | | | |
|---|---|---|---|
| 1 + 1 = ☐ | 1 + 1 = ☐ | 2 + 1 = ☐ | 1 + 2 = ☐ |
| 2 + 1 = ☐ | 1 + 2 = ☐ | 2 + 2 = ☐ | 2 + 2 = ☐ |
| 3 + 1 = ☐ | 1 + 3 = ☐ | 2 + 3 = ☐ | 3 + 2 = ☐ |
| 4 + 1 = ☐ | 1 + 4 = ☐ | 2 + 4 = ☐ | 4 + 2 = ☐ |
| 5 + 1 = ☐ | 1 + 5 = ☐ | 2 + 5 = ☐ | 5 + 2 = ☐ |

## Plenary

- Together, look at the additions and their patterns.

- Invite the children to say what the answers are and what the next lines in each pattern should be.

- Ask them to describe any patterns they noticed in each addition.

# Properties of Number (3)

**Outcome**

*Children will be able to use counting in twos and tens to solve addition problems*

## Medium-term plan objectives

- Count in tens from and back to zero.
- Count on in twos from zero.
- Begin to recognise even numbers.
- Read and write numerals from 0 to at least 20.
- Know what each digit in a two-digit number represents.
- Begin to partition larger two-digit numbers into a multiple of 10 and ones.
- Say the number that is 1 or 10 more or less than any given number to 20.

## Overview

- Counting in tens.
- Counting in twos.
- Partitioning numbers into tens and ones.
- Using physical apparatus to make 1 or 10 more.

## How you could plan this unit

| | Stage 1 | Stage 2 | Stage 3 | Stage 4 | Stage 5 |
|---|---|---|---|---|---|
| Content and vocabulary | Count on in tens from zero, and count back in tens to zero<br><br>*counting in tens, numbers names and numerals for 0, 10, 20 and so on to 100* | Counting in twos and recognising even numbers<br><br>*counting in twos, even numbers* | Knowing the value of a digit and partitioning two-digit numbers<br><br>*tens and units, partition, combine* | Using cubes to make numbers that are 1 or 10 more than a number | |
| Notes | | Resource page A | | | |

# Count on in tens from zero, and count back in tens to zero

**Advance Organiser**

We are going to count in tens

**Oral/mental starter
p 181**

**You will need:** washing line and pegs, 1 to 100 number grid (enlarged), number cards for tens from 0 to 100 (one per child and one enlarged), blank track to fit 11 number cards (one per child)

## Whole-class work

- Display the 1 to 100 grid.
- Together, say the numbers in sequence as far as you think the children can.
- Ask the children to suggest patterns they can see in the numbers on the grid.
- Point to different numbers in turn.
- *What is this number?*
- After a few goes, point, in turn, to 10, 20, 30 and so on to 100.
- *What is this number?*
- As you say each number hang the appropriate tens number card on the washing line with 10 on the left.
- *Who can tell me about these numbers?*
- When complete, explain that the numbers are *counting in tens numbers*.
- Show them how they are similar to the numbers 1 to 10.
- Point to each number in turn and count in a rhythmical manner with the class.
- Repeat without pointing, then repeat while children cover their eyes.
- Remove one or more numbers.
- *What number goes here?*
- Point to each number in turn starting with 100 counting back.
- Introduce zero and put the zero card at the far left.
- Count back with the class in tens, then secretly remove a number and ask which you have removed.

## Independent, paired or group work

- Give each pair a set of tens cards and a blank number track.
- Ask them to order the cards and repeat the 'missing number' game above in their pairs, one child playing your role.
- Another game is to ask the children to place the zero card in its position and place the other cards face down on the table.
- In turn each child turns over a card and places it in its correct position in the grid.

## Plenary

- Place 11 pegs on the washing line. Hang the zero on the far left.
- Give a child one of the numbers 0 to 100.
- *What is your number? Hang it in its correct place.*
- Repeat the activity with 100 hanging in the far right position.

# Counting in twos and recognising even numbers

**Advance Organiser**

We are going to count in twos and look for even numbers

**Oral/mental starter p 181**

**You will need:** 1 to 20 number cards pegged on a washing line, 0–20 number track (enlarged), resource page A (one per child)

## Whole-class work

- Practise counting forward and back on the number line.
- Turn over the odd number cards to their blank sides.
- *Tell me a number that is still showing.*
- Together say the numbers 2, 4 and so on as you point to them.
- Explain to the children that they are counting in twos. Ask them to tell you what this means.
- Practise counting in twos including counting back if appropriate.
- Tell them that the numbers 2, 4, 6 and so on to 20 are called even numbers. (At this stage do not explain this in terms of division.)
- Show the children the enlarged 0 to 20 number track.
- Put a toy frog or similar at zero. Explain that the frog is going to make a jump of 2.
- *What number will he land on? He jumped to land on 2.*
- Demonstrate jumping a single jump of 2, not 2 jumps of 1.
- Repeat up to 20.
- Confirm that these are *even numbers*.

| 0 | 1 | 2 | 3 | 4 | 5 | 6 | 7 | 8 | 9 | 10 | 11 | 12 | 13 | 14 | 15 | 16 | 17 | 18 | 19 | 20 |

## Independent, paired or group work

- Give each child a copy of resource page A.
- Use the first number grid to show them how to count on in twos from zero and to colour in each number they land on.
- Ask them to do the same for each of the grids.

## Plenary

- Draw a table as shown and explain how it is used to sort.
- Have the cards 0 to 20 in a pile face down in random order.
- Turn over the top card.
- *Is this an even number?*
- Sort the numbers on the sorting grid.
- Ask the children to help you order each set of numbers.
- End by using the sorted numbers to count on using the even numbers and the 'odd' numbers.

| is an even number | is not an even number |
|---|---|
|  |  |

# Number grids

| 0 | 1 | 2 | 3 | 4 |
|---|---|---|---|---|
| 5 | 6 | 7 | 8 | 9 |
| 10 | 11 | 12 | 13 | 14 |
| 15 | 16 | 17 | 18 | 19 |
| 20 | 21 | | | |

| 0 | 1 | 2 | 3 |
|---|---|---|---|
| 4 | 5 | 6 | 7 |
| 8 | 9 | 10 | 11 |
| 12 | 13 | 14 | 15 |
| 16 | 17 | 18 | 19 |
| 20 | 21 | | |

| 0 | 1 | 2 | 3 | 4 | 5 | 6 | 7 | 8 | 9 |
|---|---|---|---|---|---|---|---|---|---|
| 10 | 11 | 12 | 13 | 14 | 15 | 16 | 17 | 18 | 19 |
| 20 | 21 | | | | | | | | |

| 0 | 1 |
|---|---|
| 2 | 3 |
| 4 | 5 |
| 6 | 7 |
| 8 | 9 |
| 10 | 11 |
| 12 | 13 |
| 14 | 15 |
| 16 | 17 |
| 18 | 19 |
| 20 | 21 |

# Knowing the value of a digit and partitioning two-digit numbers

**Advance Organiser**

We are going to work with two-digit numbers

**Oral/mental starter p 181**

**You will need:** 10 to 40 number cards (one set), linking cubes, 0 to 30 number cards (per child)

## Whole-class work

- Hold up the 15 number card. *What number am I holding up?*
- Ask the children to use their number cards as digits to make this number.
- *How many tens has the number 15? How many units has the number 15?*
- Confirm that the 1 digit in this number represents *one ten* and the 5 digit in this number makes *five ones*.
- Ask the children to count out 15 linking cubes.
- *Make a 10-stick and some units with your 15 cubes.*
- *How many 10-sticks have you? How many units (ones) have you?*
- Record on the board: *15 is the same as 1 ten and 5 units.*
- Repeat with other numbers from 10 to 30.
- Ask a child to make you a 10-stick.
- *How many more cubes do I need so that I have twelve cubes altogether?*
- Record on the board as *10 + 2 = 12.*
- Repeat for 24 with two 10-sticks and four cubes.
- Count out 13 cubes and ask a child to make them into a 10-stick and some units.
- Show them that 13 has the same value as 10 and 3.
- Record this on the board.
- Repeat this with 25 cubes.
- Make sure that they understand that two 10-sticks has the same value as 20 individual cubes.

## Independent, paired or group work

- Give the children selected number cards to repeat the above steps for themselves. Ask them to keep each number card together with the 10-sticks and unit cubes that represent that number.

## Plenary

- Write these additions on the board.
- Question the children about the missing numbers.
- Remind them that a two-digit number can be broken down into a number of tens and units.
- Also remind them that a number of tens and units can be combined to make a two-digit number.

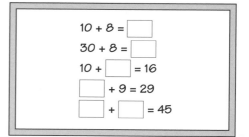

$$10 + 8 = \boxed{\phantom{0}}$$
$$30 + 8 = \boxed{\phantom{0}}$$
$$10 + \boxed{\phantom{0}} = 16$$
$$\boxed{\phantom{0}} + 9 = 29$$
$$\boxed{\phantom{0}} + \boxed{\phantom{0}} = 45$$

18

# Using cubes to make numbers that are 1 or 10 more than a number

**Advance Organiser**

We are going to find numbers that are 10 more than other numbers

**Oral/mental starter p 181**

**You will need:** linking cubes for you, 1 to 100 number grid (one per child and one enlarged)

## Whole-class work

- Hold up a 10-stick and four cubes.
- *How many cubes have I altogether?*
- With the class, count the cubes to check children's 'guesses'.
- Circle the 14 on the enlarged 1 to 100 grid.
- *How many cubes will I have when I add 1 more cube to the 14?*
- Add 1 more cube to the 14 and together count how many cubes there are.
- Put a circle around 15 and draw an arrow from 14 to 15. Record on the board.
- Repeat for other numbers.
- Talk about the position of a number that is 1 more than another number.
- Point to 26 on the 100 square.

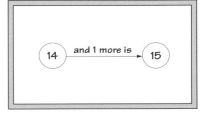

- *Where is the number that is 1 more than 26? What is the number that is 1 more than 26?*
- Repeat for other numbers.
- Hold up a 10-stick and eight cubes.
- *How many cubes have I altogether?*
- Circle the 18 on the enlarged 100 square.
- *How many cubes will I have when I add 10 more cubes to the 18?*
- Make a 10-stick and add it to the 18.
- Together count how many cubes there are. Count 10, 20, 21, 22 and so on to 28.
- Put a circle around 28 and draw an arrow from 18 to 28. Record on the board.
- Repeat for other numbers.
- Talk about the position of a number that is 10 more than another number.
- Point to 3 on the 100 square.
- *Where is the number that is 10 more than 3? What is the number?*

## Independent, paired or group work

- Give the children practice questions finding 1 more and 10 more.

## Plenary

- Using different numbers, ask what is 1 more than the number.
- Ask them where to find a number on their grid that is 1 more than a given number.
- Do the same for numbers that are 10 more.

# Properties of Number (4)

### Outcome

*Children will be able to use fives and twos number patterns to solve problems*

| | |
|---|---|
| **Medium-term plan objectives** | • Count on in twos from zero, then one, and begin to recognise odd and even numbers to 10. |
| | • Count in steps of 5 from zero to 20 or more. |
| | • Solve mathematical problems or puzzles. |
| | • Suggest extensions by asking *'What if ...?'* or *'What could I try next?'* |
| **Overview** | • Identifying odd and even numbers. |
| | • Counting in fives. |
| | • Splitting a number into twos. |
| | • Using knowledge of the number system to solve problems. |

## How you could plan this unit

| | Stage 1 | Stage 2 | Stage 3 | Stage 4 | Stage 5 |
|---|---|---|---|---|---|
| **Content and vocabulary** | Count on in twos leading to odd and even numbers<br><br>*zero, even, odd, pattern, sorting, set* | Counting in fives<br><br>*count in fives, sequence, missing numbers, pattern* | Making as many 2-sticks as possible with a given number of cubes<br><br>*2-sticks, left over, order* | Solving a problem about 'next to' numbers<br><br>*next to, number circles* | |
| **Notes** | | Resource pages A and B | | Resource pages C and D | |

# Count on in twos leading to odd and even numbers

**Advance Organiser**

We are going to find out about odd and even numbers

**Oral/mental starter p 181**

You will need: 0 to 30 number track, blank number cards, 0 to 10 number cards, 0 to 20 number cards (one per pair)

## Whole-class work

- Point to zero on the 0 to 30 number track.
- *What is the name of this number? We are going to start counting from zero.*
- Point to every counting number up to 30.
- Tell the children that this time you are going to miss out some numbers and they must only say the numbers you point to. Point to 0, 2, 4 and so on to 30.
- *Tell me how I counted this time. Which numbers did we miss out?*
- Cover up each of the odd numbers as you are told them with the blank cards.
- Together, count the numbers that are left without you pointing.
- *These numbers have a special name. What is it?*
- Write the numbers on the board like this.
- *Tell me any patterns you can see in the even numbers.*
- *What is the next even number after 30?*
- Repeat for 32, 34, 36, 38 writing the numbers in the box each time.

| 0 | 10 | 20 | 30 |
|---|----|----|----|
| 2 | 12 | 22 |    |
| 4 | 14 | 24 |    |
| 6 | 16 | 26 |    |
| 8 | 18 | 28 |    |

- Remove the blank cards so that the odd numbers are showing. Point to one.
- Repeat the exercise above with the odd numbers.
- *These numbers are NOT even numbers, but they have a special name. What is it?*
- Write the numbers on the board in a box at the side of the even numbers.
- Explain how you have written the even numbers.
- *Tell me any patterns you can see in the odd numbers. What is the next odd number after 29?*
- Repeat for 31, 33, 35, 37 writing the numbers in the box each time.

| 0 | 10 | 20 | 30 |   | 1 | 11 | 21 |
|---|----|----|----|---|---|----|----|
| 2 | 12 | 22 |    |   | 3 | 13 | 23 |
| 4 | 14 | 24 |    |   | 5 | 15 | 25 |
| 6 | 16 | 26 |    |   | 7 | 17 | 27 |
| 8 | 18 | 28 |    |   | 9 | 19 | 29 |

## Independent, paired or group work

- Ask each pair to sort the number cards 0 to 20 into sets of odd and even numbers.

## Plenary

- In turn, randomly hold up number cards 0 to 10.
- *Is this an even number or an odd number?*

# Counting in fives

**Advance Organiser**

We are going to count in fives

**Oral/mental starter p 181**

**You will need:** linking cubes, washing line and pegs, number cards for 0, 5, 10 and so on up to 30, resource page A (one per child and one enlarged), resource page B (one per child)

## Whole-class work

- Count out five cubes with the children.

- Make them into a 5-stick.

- *How many cubes are in the stick altogether?*

- Show the 5-stick card made from an enlarged version of resource page A.

- Show them two 5-sticks of linking cubes.

- Count with the class how many cubes altogether in the two sticks. Show them the two 5-sticks card.

- Repeat with 3, 4, 5 and 6 sticks.

- Show in turn 5-stick cards for 15 to 30.

- Each time ask: *How many cubes are there altogether?*

- Leave the cards in order 5, 10, 15, 20, 25, 30.

- Show the children the blank card.

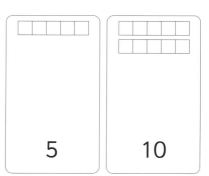

- *How many cubes on this card? Where should we put this card in the sequence?*

- Together say the numbers 0, 5, 10, 15, 20, 25, 30.

- *What steps are we counting in?*

- Peg up the number cards 0, 5 and so on to 30 on a washing line.

- Practise counting on and back in fives.

- *What patterns can you see in the count in fives sequence?*

- Cover up one or more numbers.

- *What are the numbers that I have covered up?*

- Cover up all the number cards.

- Together count on and back in fives.

## Independent, paired or group work

- Give the children resource page B to complete.

## Plenary

- Put the 5-stick cards for 0 to 30 on the washing line in a random order.

- Ask the children to put them in order.

- Repeat the activity with the number cards for 0 to 30.

## Counting in fives

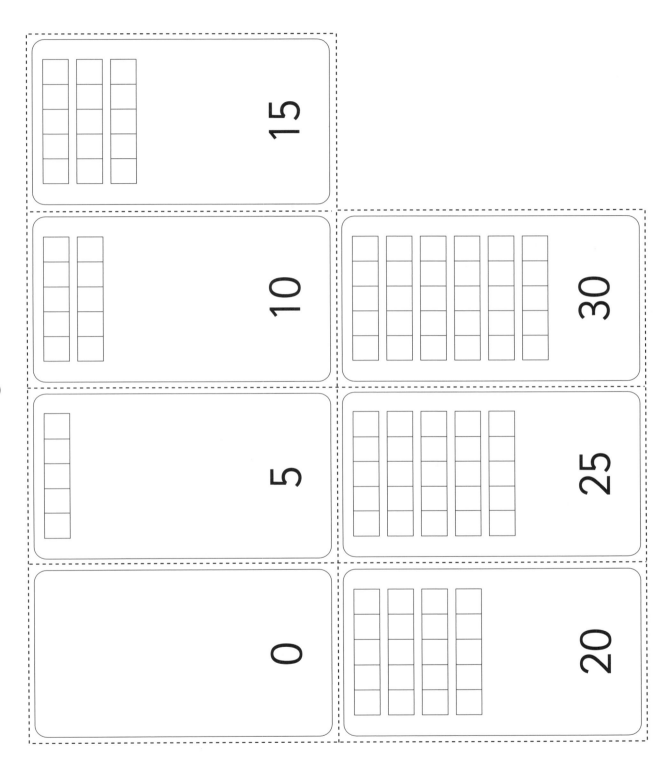

15

10

30

5

25

0

20

Name: _____

# Counting in fives

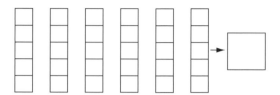

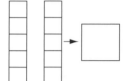

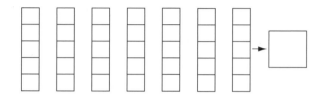

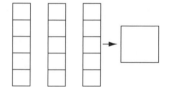

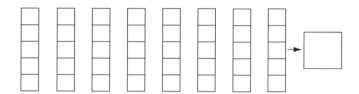

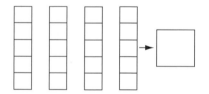

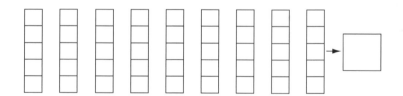

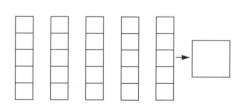

Complete this sequence

| 0 | → | 5 | → | 10 | → | | → | | → | | → | | → | | → | | → | | → | |

# *Making as many 2-sticks as possible with a given number of cubes*

**Advance Organiser**

We are going to solve a mathematical problem about making 2-sticks

**Oral/mental starter p 181**

**You will need:** linking cubes

## Whole-class work

- Choose 12 linking cubes. Show them to the children.
- Together, count the number of cubes.
- Write on the board: *I have 12 cubes.*
- *I am going to make as many 2-sticks as I can with the 12 cubes.*
- *Will I have any cubes over? How can you tell?*
- Make six 2-sticks with the 12 cubes.
- Repeat the activity with nine cubes.
- Each child counts out 16 cubes.
- *You are going to make 2-sticks with your 16 cubes.*
- *Do you think you will have any left over? How can you tell?*
- They make the 2-sticks.
- Repeat the activity with 11 cubes.

## Independent, paired or group work

- Each child counts out five cubes.
- On paper they draw the cubes (as squares) and write the number alongside.
- They make as many 2-sticks as they can with the five cubes and then draw the resulting two 2-sticks and a single cube.
- Ask them to do the same for numbers 6 to 9.

## Plenary

- Draw this table on the board.
- Discuss the numbers in the first column and how they are in order.
- Use the children's experience from the early activities to complete the chart by ringing either Yes or No.
- Ask what they notice about the Yes/No answers that are circled.
- You may wish to talk about these generalisations: when making 2-sticks there is either 0 or 1 cubes left over; an even number of cubes has 0 cubes left over when making 2-sticks; an odd number of cubes has 1 cube left over when making 2-sticks.

| Number of cubes | Are any left over? |
|---|---|
| 5 | Yes No |
| 6 | Yes No |
| 7 | Yes No |
| 8 | Yes No |
| 9 | Yes No |
| 10 | Yes No |
| 11 | Yes No |
| 12 | Yes No |

# Solving a problem about 'next to' numbers

**Advance Organiser**

We are going to solve a mathematical problem about 'next to' numbers

**Oral/mental starter**
**p 181**

**You will need:** resource page C (enlarged), number circles cut from the same page, resource page D (one per child)

## Whole-class work

- Draw on the board a number track from 1 to 4.

- Talk about the numbers that are next to each other.

- *What number is next to 2?*

- *What other number is next to 2?*

| 1 | 2 | 3 | 4 |

- Show the children an enlarged copy of resource page C. Place the number circles 1, 2, 3 and 4 as shown.

- Discuss which pairs of numbers are 'next to' numbers (2 and 1, 4 and 3).

- *I have a challenge for you. I want you to come out and place a number card in each circle, but this time any two numbers that are 'next to each other' numbers must not be next to each other on our diagram.*

- Give a few children a chance to try the challenge.

## Independent, paired or group work

- Give each pair a copy of resource page D and the number circles 1 to 4 from resource page C.

- Tell them to try the challenge using their number circles.

- Show them how to record their attempt on the recording part of resource page D, putting a ring around 'correct' or 'not correct' after each try.

## Plenary

- Ask the children to show the rest of the class a correct arrangement.

- There are only two, reversals of each other.

- Ask the children what they think might happen if they had five numbers and five circles.

- Suggest they try to do this at home with the second half of resource page C.

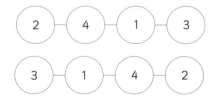

CUT-OUT

# Number circles

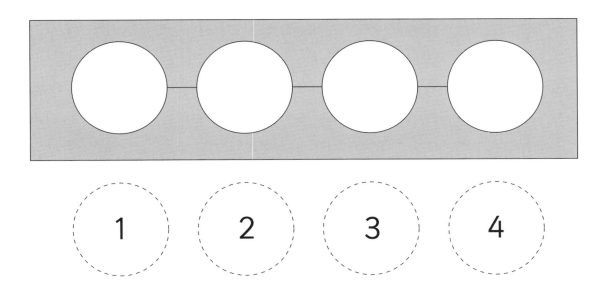

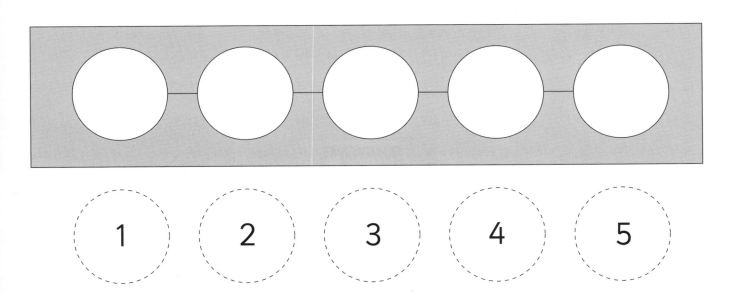

**EXAMPLE**

# 'Next to' numbers

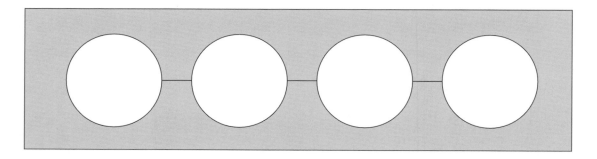

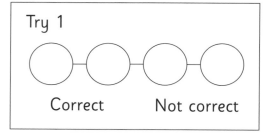

Try 1

Correct     Not correct

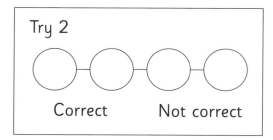

Try 2

Correct     Not correct

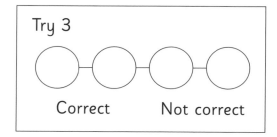

Try 3

Correct     Not correct

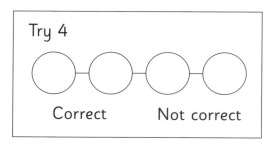

Try 4

Correct     Not correct

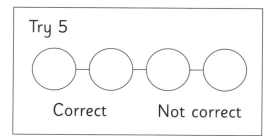

Try 5

Correct     Not correct

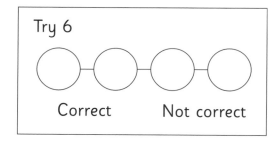

Try 6

Correct     Not correct

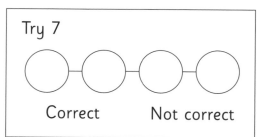

Try 7

Correct     Not correct

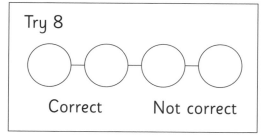

Try 8

Correct     Not correct

# Properties of Number (5)

**Outcome**

*Children will be able to recognise patterns on a number grid and compare numbers less than 10*

**Medium-term plan objectives**

- Recognise odd and even numbers to 20 as *'every other number'*.
- Count in steps of 5 from zero to 20 or more and then back again.
- Say the number that is one or ten more or less than a given number to 30.
- Compare two familiar numbers, say which is more or less, and give a number that lies between them.

**Overview**

- Recognising odd and even numbers on a grid.
- Counting in fives on a grid.
- Finding more, less and between numbers.

## How you could plan this unit

| | Stage 1 | Stage 2 | Stage 3 | Stage 4 | Stage 5 |
|---|---|---|---|---|---|
| **Content and vocabulary** | Colouring even and odd numbers on a 0 to 49 number grid | Counting on in fives using a 0 to 99 number grid | More, less and between | | |
| | *red, yellow, even number, odd number* | *count on in fives, count back in fives, pattern in unit digits* | *more than, less than, fewer than, between* | | |
| **Notes** | | | | | |

# Colouring even and odd numbers on a 0 to 49 number grid

**Advance Organiser**

We are going to colour even and odd numbers on a number grid

**Oral/mental starter p 181**

**You will need:** red and yellow crayons (for you and per child), 0 to 49 number grid (one per child and one enlarged)

## Whole-class work

- Show the children the enlarged 0 to 49 number grid.
- *Find the number 23.*
- Repeat for other numbers.
- Colour 0 red. *What number have I coloured red?*
- Repeat for 2, 4, 6 and 8.
- *I am going to colour more numbers red.*
- *What is the next one I shall colour red? Tell me how you decided.*
- *I am colouring every other number red starting with 0.*
- Colour 10, 12 and 14 red.
- *What is the special name for the numbers that are red?*
- Colour 1 yellow. *What number have I coloured yellow?*
- Repeat for 3, 5, 7 and 9.
- *I am going to colour more numbers yellow.*
- *What is the next one I shall colour yellow? Tell me how you decided.*
- *I am colouring every other number yellow starting with 1.*
- Colour 11, 13, and 15 yellow.
- *What is the special name for the numbers that are yellow?*

| 0 | 1 | 2 | 3 | 4 | 5 | 6 | 7 |
|---|---|---|---|---|---|---|---|
| 8 | 9 | 10 | 11 | 12 | 13 | 14 | 15 |
| 16 | 17 | 18 | 19 | 20 | 21 | 22 | 23 |
| 24 | 25 | 26 | 27 | 28 | 29 | 30 | 31 |
| 32 | 33 | 34 | 35 | 36 | 37 | 38 | 39 |
| 40 | 41 | 42 | 43 | 44 | 45 | 46 | 47 |
| 48 | 49 | | | | | | |

## Independent, paired or group work

- Tell the children to colour red all the even numbers on their 0 to 49 grid.
- Talk about the pattern of the red (even) numbers.
- When they have finished, tell them to colour yellow all the odd numbers.

## Plenary

- Ask the children to tell you about the patterns that the even and odd numbers make on their grid.
- Draw on the board an 'even numbers' and an 'odd numbers' enclosure.
- Show a blank copy of the gid.
- Point to different numbers in turn.
- *Is this an even number or an odd number?*
- Write each number in its correct enclosure.
- Point to the even enclosure.
- *Tell me a number that belongs in the even number enclosure.*
- Repeat for odd numbers.

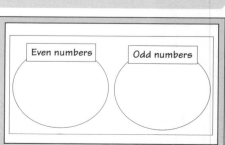

# Counting on in fives using a 0 to 99 number grid

**Advance Organiser**

We are going to investigate counting on in fives

**Oral/mental starter p 181**

**You will need:** blue crayon (for you and per child), 0 to 99 number grid (one per pair and one enlarged)

## Whole-class work

- Show the children the enlarged 0 to 99 number grid.
- *Who can show me the number 48?*
- Repeat for other numbers.
- Point to 0. *This is the start number and I am colouring this blue.*
- *Together we are going to count forward five, stop, and then colour in the number we land on.*
- Together count 1, 2, 3, 4, 5 and stop. Colour 5 blue.
- *What number have I coloured blue?*
- *I am going to count on five more.*
- *What do you think the next number will be that I will colour blue? Tell me how you decided.*
- Ask the children to count on five and colour the number they end at.
- Continue until 25 is coloured.
- *We can make a sequence with the blue numbers.*
- Point to each blue number in turn.
- *What is this number?*
- Write each number on the board in the sequence.
- Together, count on in fives from 0 and back in fives from 25.
- Remove the sequence from the board.
- Together, count on in fives continuing past 25 until most of the children have stopped.

*0  5  10  15  20  25*

## Independent, paired or group work

- Each child counts on five starting at 0 on a 0 to 99 number grid and colours in blue every number they land on.

## Plenary

- Ask the children to tell you a number that is in the count-on in fives sequence.
- Some may need to use their number square.
- *Is 23 in the count-on in fives sequence?* Repeat for other numbers.
- Talk about the pattern made by the count-on in fives sequence in the number square.
- In turn, point to the blue numbers that end in 0.
- *What is the pattern in the units digit in these numbers?*
- Repeat for the blue numbers with 5 as the unit digit.

# More, less and between

**Advance Organiser**

We are going to find out which of two numbers is more and which is less

Oral/mental starter p 181

**You will need:** linking cubes (for you and per child), 1 to 10 number track (for you and per child), number cards 1 to 20

## Whole-class work

- Ask the children to make a 4-stick and a 7-stick with linking cubes.

- Choose a child to count how many cubes are in each of their sticks.

- Label the sticks with a 4 and a 7 number card.

- *Which stick has more cubes? How did you decide?*

- Write on the board: *7 is more than 4.*

- Together, look at the 1 to 10 number track.

- Invite a child to show you where 4 and 7 are.

- *How do the positions of the 4 and 7 tell you which is more and which is less?*

- *Which has fewer cubes, the 4-stick or the 7-stick?*

- Write on the board: *4 is less than 7.*

- Repeat with a 9-stick and a 3-stick.

- Show the 3-stick and the 9-stick side by side with a gap between.

- *I want you to make a stick that has more cubes than the 3-stick and not as many as the 9-stick.*

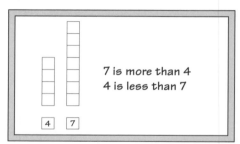

- Invite the children to show the stick they have made, say a 5-stick, and their 3-stick and 9-stick.

- Ask them to test their stick by placing it between the other two sticks.

- Write on the board: *5 is between 3 and 9.*

- Do the same for 4, 6, 7 and 8 if the children suggest them.

- Ask a child to show where 3 and 9 are on the 1 to 10 number track.

- *What numbers are between 3 and 9?*

- Point to each statement on the board to confirm the numbers 4, 5, 6, 7 and 8.

## Independent, paired or group work

- Give children practice statements to complete for pairs of numbers between 1 and 10, such as *2 is (more/less) than 7*; ☐ *is between 3 and 6.*

## Plenary

- Use the 1 to 10 number cards. In turn hold up two numbers (not adjacent).

- *Which number is more/Which number is less? Tell me how you decided.*

- *Tell me a number that is between the two numbers. Tell me how you decided.*

- Extend to using the 11 to 20 number cards.

# Properties of Number (6)

**Outcome**

*Children will be able to predict and extend sequences in ones, twos and threes*

**Medium-term plan objectives**

- Begin to count on in steps of 3 from zero.
- Recognise and extend sequences with differences of 1, 2 or 3.

**Overview**

- Building a sequence by adding 1.
- Building a sequence by adding 2.
- Building a sequence by adding 3.
- Ordering a set of numbers into a sequence.

## How you could plan this unit

| | Stage 1 | Stage 2 | Stage 3 | Stage 4 | Stage 5 |
|---|---|---|---|---|---|
| **Content and vocabulary** | Making and extending add 1 sequences | Making and extending add 2 sequences | Making and extending add 3 sequences | Ordering a set of numbers to make a sequence | |
| | *1 more, add 1 sequence, sequence, pattern, extend a sequence* | *2 more, add 2 sequence, sequence, pattern, extend a sequence* | *count on 3, start at, sequence, pattern, extend a sequence* | *order, smallest/largest, count on/back, start, number, sequence, name of a sequence* | |
| **Notes** | Resource page A | Resource page B | Resource page C | | |

# *Making and extending add 1 sequences*

**Advance Organiser**

We are going to build towers that make patterns and sequences

**Oral/mental starter p 181**

**You will need:** linking cubes, number cards 1 to 40, washing line and pegs, resource page A (one per child)

## Whole-class work

- Show the sequence of towers 1, 2, 3, 4 and 5 of linking cubes.

- Make each tower a different colour.

- *How many cubes are there in each tower?*

- Label each tower with the correct number of cubes.

- Ask the children to build the towers.

- Together, say the sequence of cubes in each tower.

- *Build the next tower in the sequence.*

- *How did you know how many cubes were in the next tower?*

- Repeat for two more towers.

- Discuss that the number of cubes in a tower is 1 more than the previous tower.

- *To make a new tower we add 1 more cube to the number in the previous tower. It is an add 1 sequence.*

- Put the number card sequence 8, 9, 10, 11 and 12 on the washing line.

- *What is the next number in the sequence. How did you work it out?*

- Ask a child to put the number card on the washing line.

- Repeat for four more numbers.

- Do the same for the following sequences: 15, 16, 17, 18, 19; 22, 23, 24, 25, 26; 31, 32, 33, 34, 35.

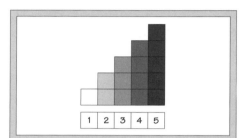

## Independent, paired or group work

- Show the children resource page A.

- Explain that they have to extend each washing line sequence by writing what the next three numbers should be on the blank cards.

## Plenary

- Ask the children in turn to say how they extended a sequence and how they worked it out.

Name: _____

# Add 1 sequences

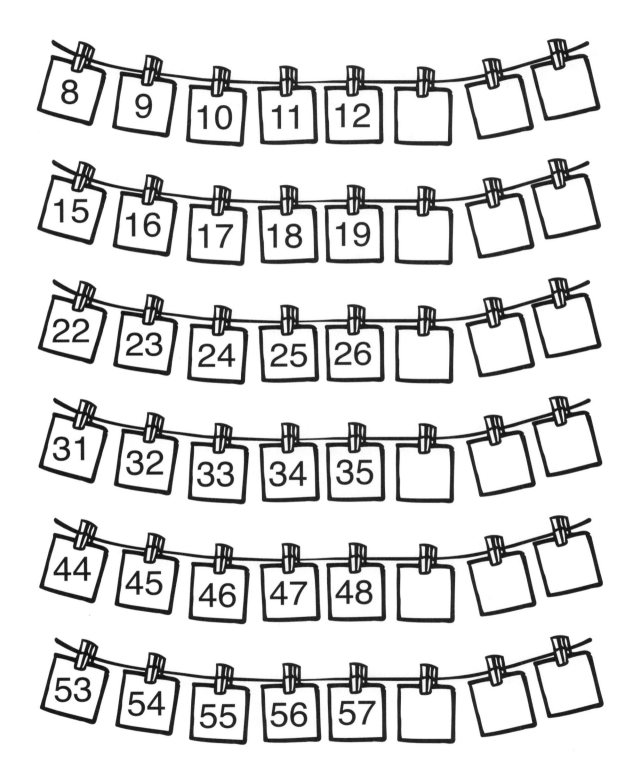

# Making and extending add 2 sequences

**Advance Organiser**

We are going to build more towers that make patterns and sequences

**Oral/mental starter p 181**

**You will need:** linking cubes (for you and per child), set of number cards 1 to 40, washing line and pegs, resource page B (one per child)

## Whole-class work

- Show the sequence of towers 2, 4, 6, 8 and 10 of linking cubes.

- Make each tower a different colour.

- Point to the first four towers in turn.

- *How many cubes are this tower?*

- Label them.

- Say the numbers 2, 4, 6, 8.

- *How many cubes are in the last tower?*

- Label the tower.

- Ask the children to build the towers.

- Together, say the sequence of cubes in each tower.

- *Build the next tower in the sequence.*

- *How did you know how many cubes were in the next tower?*

- Repeat for two more towers.

- Discuss that the number of cubes in a tower is 2 more than the previous tower.

- *To make a new tower we add 2 more cubes to the number in the previous tower. It is an add 2 sequence.*

- Put the number card sequence 6, 8, 10, 12 and 14 on the washing line.

- *What is the next number in the sequence. How did you work it out?*

- Ask a child to put the number card on the washing line.

- Repeat for four more numbers.

- Do the same for the sequences: 12, 14, 16, 18, 20; 15, 17, 19, 21, 23; 31, 33, 35, 37, 39.

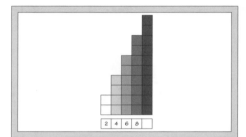

## Independent, paired or group work

- Show the children resource page B.

- Explain that they have to extend each snake sequence by writing what the next three numbers should be on the blank spaces.

## Plenary

- Ask the children in turn to say how they extended a sequence and how they worked it out.

Name: _____

# Add 2 sequences

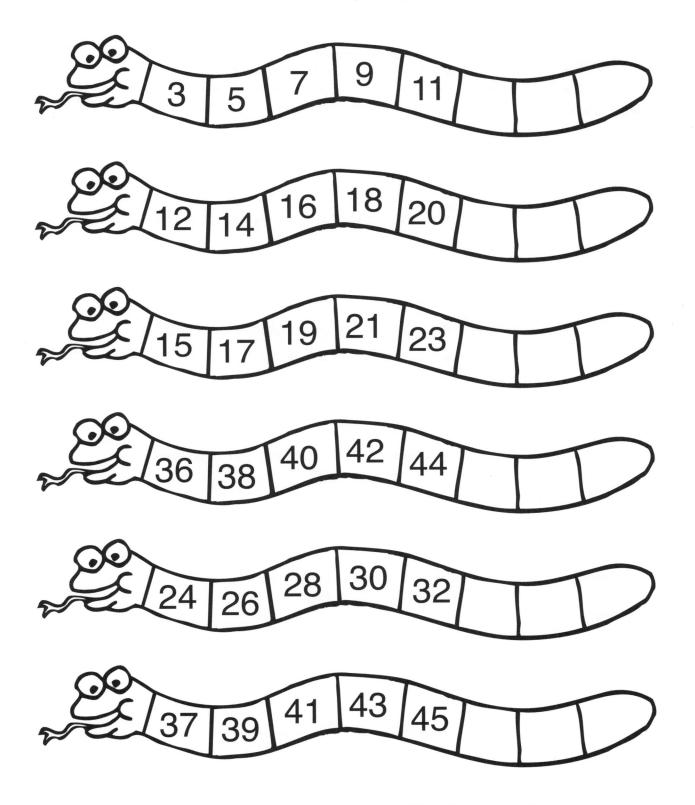

# *Making and extending add 3 sequences*

**Advance Organiser**

We are going to build towers that make patterns and sequences

**Oral/mental starter p 181**

**You will need:** 0 to 30 number cards (for you and per child), washing line and pegs, resource page C per child (one per child)

## Whole-class work

- Put the number cards 0 to 15 on the washing line.

- *I am starting at 0 and counting on 3. What number will I stop at?*

- *When we count on 3 again what number will we stop at?*

- Repeat to 15.

- *What numbers did we stop at when we started at 0 and counted on 3?*

- Take the numbers from the line and put them on the board in the sequence.

- *This is the count on 3 sequence starting at 0.*

- Together, say the count on 3 sequence.

- Put the 18 card at the end of the row with its face to the board.

- *Tell me the hidden number on this card. How did you work it out?*

- Ask the children to use their number cards to make the count on 3 sequence that is on the board.

- When complete, ask them to extend the sequence with three more numbers.

- You may wish them use a 1 to 100 number grid to help them.

- Repeat the count on 3 sequence above, but start at 1.

- Repeat the count on 3 sequence above, but start at 5.

## Independent, paired or group work

- Show the children resource page C.

- Explain that they have to extend each train sequence by writing what the next three numbers should be on the blank spaces.

- Some children may need the help of a 1 to 100 number grid.

## Plenary

- Ask the children in turn to say how they extended a sequence and how they worked it out.

Name: _____

# Counting on 3

*Classworks* © Classworks Numeracy author team, Nelson Thornes Ltd, 2003

# Ordering a set of numbers to make a sequence

**Advance Organiser**

We are going to order sets of numbers

**Oral/mental starter p 181**

**You will need:** number cards 1 to 20 (for you) and 1 to 40 (per child), washing line and pegs

## Whole-class work

- Put on the board the number cards 5, 7, 9, 11 and 13 in a random order.
- Point to each of the numbers in turn. Ask what the number is.
- *I want to put the numbers in order with the smallest first. Which is the smallest number?*
- Put the number on the washing line.
- In turn, ask for the next smallest, until all five numbers are on the washing line in sequence.
- *We have made a sequence. What is the sequence called?*
- Give them the full description.
- *It is a count on in twos sequence starting at 5.*
- Put the five numbers back on the board in a random order.
- *I want to put the numbers in order, but with the largest first.*
- Ask if anyone could do this. As the numbers are chosen, put them on the washing line.
- *We have made a different sequence with the same numbers. What is the sequence called?*
- Give them the full description.
- *It is a count back in twos sequence starting at 13.*

## Independent, paired or group work

- Give pairs of children sets of number cards as follows, in random order: 19, 20, 21, 22, 23; 9, 12, 15, 18, 21; 31, 33, 35, 37, 39; 15, 20, 25, 30, 35; 13, 16, 19, 22, 25.
- They should order the number cards either with the smallest first or the largest first. It is up to them to decide.
- When this is done they record the sequence they have made on paper.
- Finally, they record the name of the sequence: *count on/back in* ☐ *starting at* ☐.
- Remind them that it could be a count on or a count back sequence.

## Plenary

- Ask the children to describe a sequence that they made and to tell everyone its name.
- Ask them to explain how they did it and how they worked out its name.

# Addition and Subtraction (1)

**Outcome**

*Children will be able to record combining and taking objects from sets as addition and subtraction, and find totals by counting on*

**Medium-term plan objectives**

- Understand the operation of addition; recognise that addition can be done in any order.

- Understand the operation of subtraction (as *take away*).

- Begin to use +, − and = signs to record mental calculations in a number sentence.

- Put the larger number first.

- Count on in ones, including beyond 10 (for example, 7+5).

**Overview**

- Adding by combining two sets.

- Modelling subtraction as *taking away*.

- Adding by counting on.

## How you could plan this unit

| | Stage 1 | Stage 2 | Stage 3 | Stage 4 | Stage 5 |
|---|---|---|---|---|---|
| **Content and vocabulary** | Making and combining two sets and recording as an addition<br><br>*set, put together, altogether, addition* | Using cubes and a diagram to model taking away<br><br>*starter, take away, left over, subtraction* | Adding with and without objects to find how many altogether by counting on<br><br>*altogether, total, count on, hidden* | | |
| **Notes** | Resource page A | Resource page B | Resource page C | | |

# *Making and combining two sets and recording as an addition*

**Advance Organiser**

We are going to put two sets of cubes together to find how many

**Oral/mental starter p 181**

**You will need:** 10 cubes (for you and per child), Blu-Tack, 1 to 10 number cards, resource page A (one per pair and one enlarged)

## Whole-class work

- Show the children an enlarged copy of resource page A. Put two cubes in the left set and one cube in the right set.
- Point to each set in turn. *How many cubes in this set?*
- Use a number card to record each number in the appropriate box.
- Move the cubes from each set into the largest set explaining the meaning of the arrows.
- *I have put the cubes altogether. I am adding the cubes together.*
- You may wish to call the largest oval the 'altogether set'.
- *How many cubes are there altogether?* Record 3 in the box.
- Write on the board: *2 add 1 equals 3.* Explain that there is a special way of writing this. Write directly below the sentence: *2 + 1 = 3.* Together the children say the two expressions as you point to them.
- Ask the children what the + and = signs say.
- Explain that this is a record of what you did.
- Repeat the activity.
- *Would it make a difference if I moved these cubes first?* (Point to the right set.)
- After a while, ask the children to predict (make a good guess) how many there are altogether before they are moved into the 'altogether set'. Check by moving the cubes and counting.

## Independent, paired or group work

- Give each pair a copy of resource page A.
- Ask them to repeat the activity modelled above in their pairs.
- *What shall I write on the board to show what you have done?*
- Record as many additions as possible getting some children to explain what they did.

## Plenary

- Put five cubes in the 'altogether set'.
- *How many cubes are there altogether?*
- *How many cubes do you think were in each of the sets so that altogether they made five cubes?*
- Record the children's suggestions. Check each one.

Name: _____

# Joining together

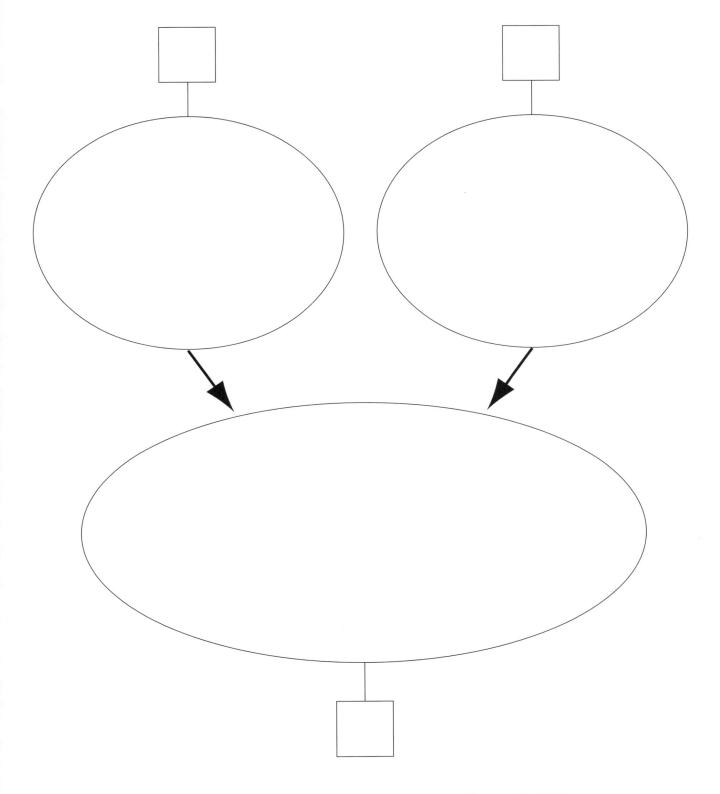

# Using cubes and a diagram to model taking away

**Advance Organiser**

We are going to see how taking away works

**Oral/mental starter pp 181–182**

**You will need:** 10 cubes (per child and for you), 1 to 10 number cards, resource page B (one per pair and one enlarged)

## Whole-class work

- Show the class an enlarged version of resource page B. You may wish to call the sets: the *starter*, the *take away* and the *left over*.

- Put five cubes in the 'starter' set. Together, count how many cubes are in the starter set. Record with the 5 number card in the box. Tell the children you are going to take two cubes away. Record a 2 in the box. Show the two cubes being taken away.

- *How many cubes have I taken away?*

- *I am putting the cubes that are left in the left over set. How many cubes are left?*

- Record a 3 in the box.

- Write: *5 take away 2 leaves 3*. Explain that there is a special way of writing this. Write directly below the sentence: *5 – 2 = 3*. Together the children say the two expressions as you point to them.

- Point to the – and = signs and ask the children what they say.

- Tell the children that taking away is sometimes called subtraction.

- Repeat the activity with different numbers of cubes.

- After a while, ask the children to predict (make a good guess) how many cubes will be left before you perform the taking away.

- Check by moving the cubes and counting.

## Independent, paired or group work

- Give each pair a copy of resource page B.

- Ask them to repeat the activity modelled above in their pairs.

- *What shall I write on the board to show what you have done?*

- Record as many subtractions as possible getting some children to explain what they did.

## Plenary

- Put four cubes in the 'left over' set.

- *How many cubes are left?*

- *How many cubes do you think there were to start with and how many were taken away?*

- Record the children's suggestions. Check each one.

- Repeat with other numbers of cubes.

Name: _____

# Take away

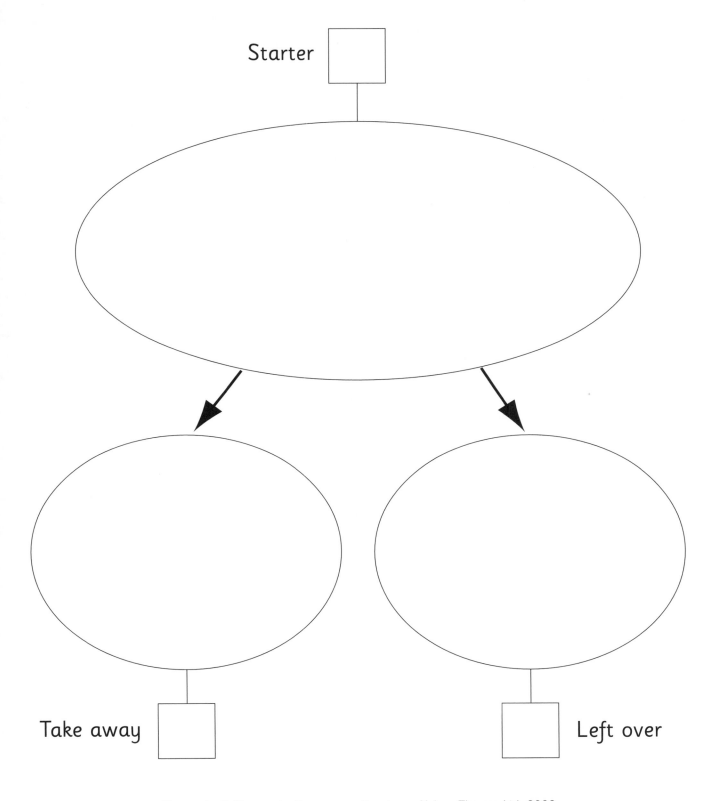

Starter

Take away

Left over

# Adding with and without objects to find how many altogether by counting on

**Advance Organiser**

We are going to find different ways of adding numbers

**Oral/mental starter pp 181–182**

**You will need:** 15 cubes (per child and for you), resource page C (enlarged: per pair and for you), 1 to 20 number cards (per child)

## Whole-class work

- Show the children an enlarged copy of resource page C.
- Put three cubes in a set and four in the other set.
- In turn point to the sets.
- *How many cubes are in the set?*
- Record each number in its box.
- *How many cubes are there altogether?*
- Record the number in the shaded box.
- Ask the children how they worked it out.
- Record on the board: *3 + 4 = 7*.
- Repeat with other pairs of numbers, including beyond 10.
- Cover up the cubes in the left-hand set. Show the children that how many altogether, the total, can still be found by counting on from 3.
- Point to the 3 and then each of the cubes in the right-hand set in turn, saying: *3, 4, 5, 6, 7. Altogether there are 7. The total number of cubes is 7.*
- You may wish to do the addition again, but with the 3 cubes visible and the 4 cubes hidden. This involves counting on from 4.

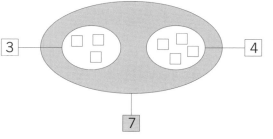

## Independent, paired or group work

- Each pair has an enlarged copy of resource page C. One child puts some cubes in each set. Using number cards the other child records how many in each set and finds how many altogether. Both children write the addition.
- Roles are then reversed. The activity is repeated, but this time only the number is placed in the left box and some cubes in the right set.

## Plenary

- Use an enlarged copy of resource page C. Put only the number cards 7 and 2 in the two boxes for adding.
- *The cubes are hidden. How many are there altogether?*
- Encourage the children to count on from 7. Record the addition on the board.
- Put 3 and 8 in the boxes.
- *How many are there altogether?*
- Ask how they did it. Encourage them to count on from the larger number.
- Repeat with other pairs of numbers.

Name:

## Addition sets

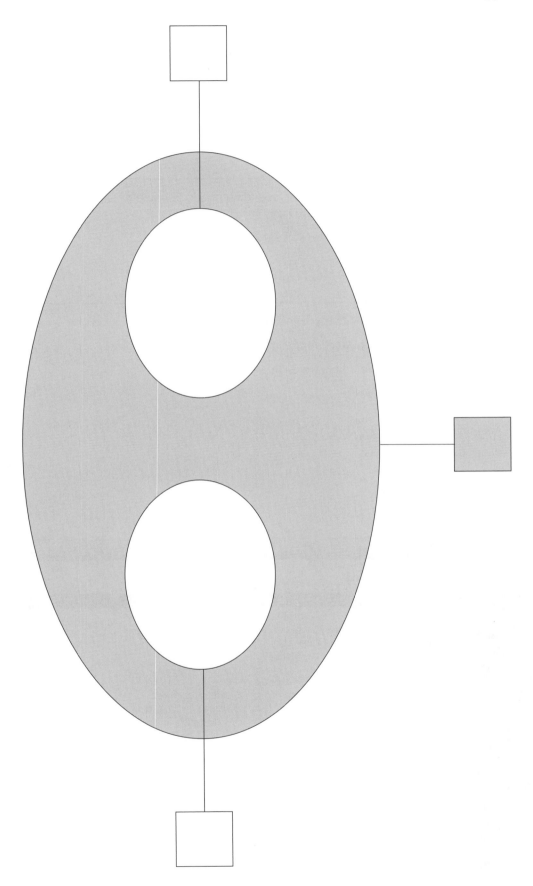

*Classworks* © Classworks Numeracy author team, Nelson Thornes Ltd, 2003

# Addition and Subtraction (2)

**Outcome**

*Children will be able to add and subtract using objects and record, and use patterns*

| Medium-term plan objectives | |
|---|---|
| | • Understand the operation of addition and of subtraction (as difference) and use related vocabulary. |
| | • Use patterns of similar calculations. |

| Overview | |
|---|---|
| | • Adding by combining sets. |
| | • Subtraction as difference. |
| | • Addition and subtraction patterns. |

## How you could plan this unit

| | Stage 1 | Stage 2 | Stage 3 | Stage 4 | Stage 5 |
|---|---|---|---|---|---|
| **Content and vocabulary** | Combining sets, counting how many altogether and recording as an addition<br><br>*how many altogether?, addition, add, equals* | Finding the number difference between two linking cube sticks and groups of objects<br><br>*number difference, difference, how many more?, how many fewer?* | Observing and using patterns in addition and subtraction<br><br>*pattern, addition, subtraction, sort, order* | | |
| **Notes** | Resource pages A and B | Resource page C | Resource pages D and E | | |

# Combining sets, counting how many altogether and recording as an addition

**Advance Organiser**

We are going to find answers to additions

**Oral/mental starter pp 181–182**

**You will need:** cubes or small objects, resource page A (enlarged), resource page B (one per child)

## Whole-class work

- Use an enlarged copy of resource page A. Put four cubes in one set and three in the other.

- Point to each set in turn.

- *How many cubes in this set?*

- Record how many in each set box.

- *How many cubes are there altogether?*

- Count them and record in the box.

- *We have added and found the answer.*

- Record in the blank addition, asking how you got each of the numbers.

- Repeat with at least two other pairs of numbers.

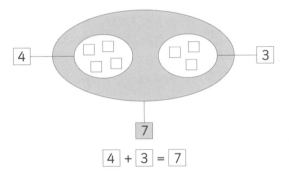

## Independent, paired or group work

- Each child has a copy of resource page B. Together work through the first question using your work on resource page A. Children then complete the first question and do the rest.

## Plenary

- Invite the children to show how they worked out how many altogether and recorded the additions.

- Encourage the process of counting on from the larger number as a quick method.

**PUPIL PAGE**

Name:

## Addition to 20

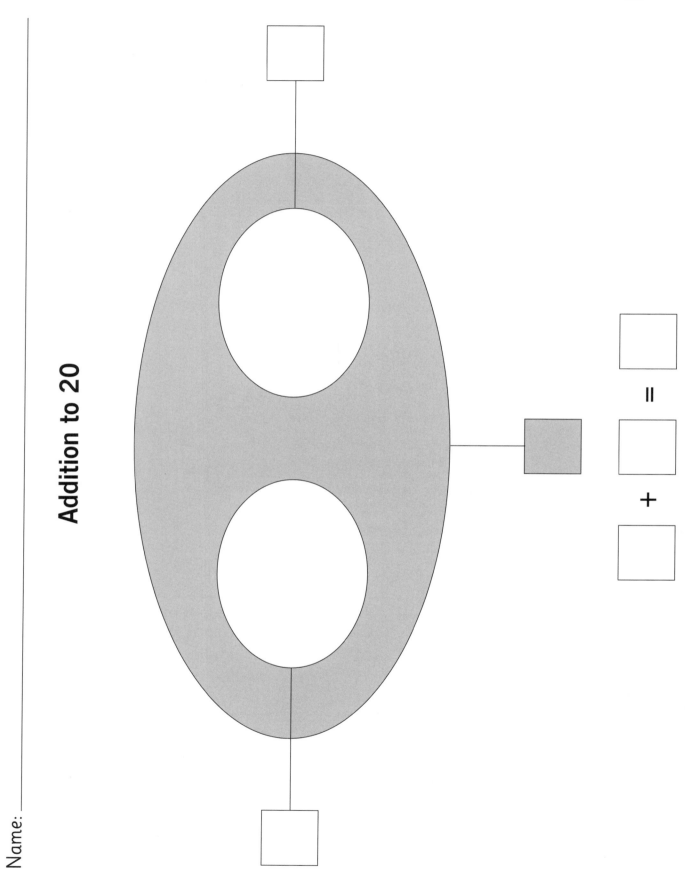

**PUPIL PAGE**

Name: _____

## How many altogether?

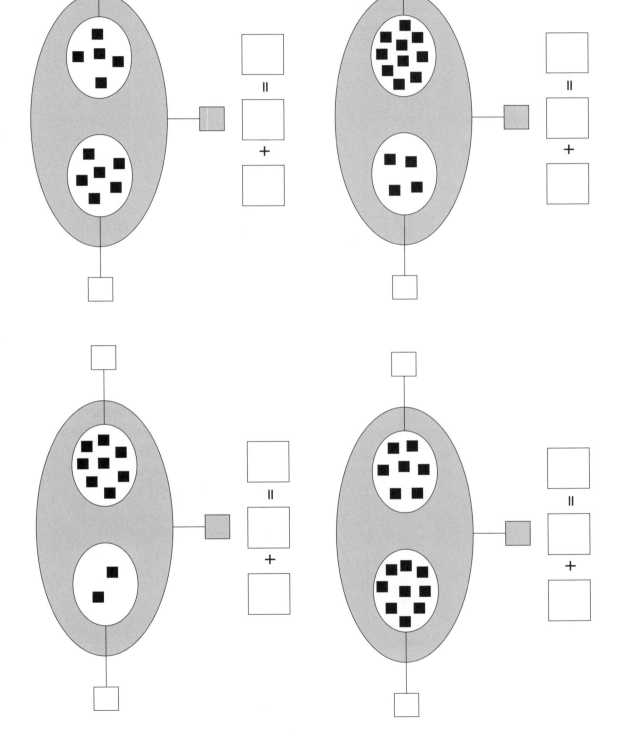

*Classworks* © Classworks Numeracy author team, Nelson Thornes Ltd, 2003

# Find the number difference between two linking cube sticks and groups of objects

**Advance Organiser**

We are going to find the number difference between two numbers

**Oral/mental starter pp 181–182**

**You will need:** linking cubes, sheets of squared paper (one for you and one per child), resource page C (one per child)

## Whole-class work

- Make a 7-stick and a 3-stick. Show them to the children.
- Hold each stick up in turn. *How many cubes in this stick?*
- *How many more cubes in the 7-stick than in the 3-stick?*
- *How many fewer cubes in the 3-stick than in the 7-stick?*
- Put the two sticks next to each other starting from the same base line.
- *How many cubes do I need to break off the 7-stick to make it equal to the 3-stick? How did you work it out?*
- Take the top four cubes off the 7-stick.
- *This is the difference between the 7-stick and the 3-stick.*
- Write on the board: *The number difference between 7 and 3 is 4.*
- Ask the children what the difference is between 3 and 7.
- Write it on the board: *The number difference between 3 and 7 is 4.*
- Explain that it does not matter which number comes first in a pair of numbers, the number difference is the same. Tell them that 'difference' is used on its own to mean 'number difference'. Repeat for other pairs of sticks.
- Draw a 9-stick and a 6-stick on squared paper. Ask how many cubes there are in each stick.
- *It is not possible to break off cubes in these drawings. How could I find the difference between the 9-stick and the 6-stick?*
- Remind the children that the difference between the two is the same number as how many more or how many fewer.
- Explain that the cubes that are more could be coloured, then counted.
- Colour three squares and count together.
- Write on the board: *The difference between 9 and 6 is 3. The difference between 6 and 9 is 3.*

## Independent, paired or group work

- Ask the children to complete resource page C. They can use squared paper.

## Plenary

- Invite the children to describe how they did the questions on resource page C.
- Stress that the difference between two numbers is the same as how many more and how many fewer.

Name: _____

# Difference between

The difference between [7] and [5] is [ ] .

The difference between [4] and [10] is [ ] .

The difference between [ ] and [ ] is [ ] .

The difference between [ ] and [ ] is [ ] .

The difference between [ ] and [ ] is [ ] .

The difference between [ ] and [ ] is [ ] .

The difference between [ ] and [ ] is [ ] .

The difference between [ ] and [ ] is [ ] .

# Observing and using patterns in addition and subtraction

**Advance Organiser**

We are going to use patterns to help us answer additions and subtractions

**Oral/mental starter pp 181–182**

**You will need:** cards made from resource pages D and E (one per child)

## Whole-class work

- Write this addition pattern on the board.

- Ask the children to find the three addition cards from resource page D that match these additions and to put the cards in front of them as they appear on the board.

- *Tell me about any patterns you can see in the additions.*

$$4 + 0 =$$
$$3 + 1 =$$
$$2 + 2 =$$

- Ask the children to find the next two additions that extend the pattern.

- Invite the children to tell you the answers to each addition. Write the answers on the board.

- *What do you notice about the answers? Why are the answers the same?*

- Tell the children to record the pattern of additions in their books.

- Repeat the activity for the subtractions as shown using cards made from resource page E.

$$3 - 0 =$$
$$4 - 1 =$$
$$5 - 2 =$$

## Independent, paired or group work

- Each pair has a set of addition cards and a sheet of A3 paper. Explain that they have to sort the additions according to their answers, in columns for answers from 0 up to 10.

- When the additions are sorted, tell the children to put each set in order.

- Early finishers can do the same for the subtraction cards.

## Plenary

- Invite the children to tell you what they have done on their table. Stress the pattern in the first and the second numbers and repeatedly explain what it is about the additions in a set that makes the answers the same.

- Repeat for any children who have sorted the subtraction cards.

CUT-OUT

# Addition cards

| | | | | | |
|---|---|---|---|---|---|
| 0 + 0 | 1 + 0 | 2 + 0 | 3 + 0 | 4 + 0 | 5 + 0 |
| 0 + 1 | 1 + 1 | 2 + 1 | 3 + 1 | 4 + 1 | 5 + 1 |
| 0 + 2 | 1 + 2 | 2 + 2 | 3 + 2 | 4 + 2 | 5 + 2 |
| 0 + 3 | 1 + 3 | 2 + 3 | 3 + 3 | 4 + 3 | 5 + 3 |
| 0 + 4 | 1 + 4 | 2 + 4 | 3 + 4 | 4 + 4 | 5 + 4 |
| 0 + 5 | 1 + 5 | 2 + 5 | 3 + 5 | 4 + 5 | 5 + 5 |
| 0 + 6 | 1 + 6 | 2 + 6 | 3 + 6 | 4 + 6 | 6 + 4 |
| 0 + 7 | 1 + 7 | 2 + 7 | 3 + 7 | 7 + 3 | 6 + 3 |
| 0 + 8 | 1 + 8 | 2 + 8 | 8 + 2 | 7 + 2 | 6 + 2 |
| 0 + 9 | 1 + 9 | 9 + 1 | 8 + 1 | 7 + 1 | 6 + 1 |
| 0 + 10 | 10 + 0 | 9 + 0 | 8 + 0 | 7 + 0 | 6 + 0 |

*Classworks* © Classworks Numeracy author team, Nelson Thornes Ltd, 2003

( CUT-OUT )

# Subtraction cards

| | | | | | |
|---|---|---|---|---|---|
| 0 – 0 | 1 – 0 | 2 – 0 | 3 – 0 | 4 – 0 | 5 – 0 |
| 1 – 1 | 2 – 1 | 3 – 1 | 4 – 1 | 5 – 1 | 6 – 1 |
| 2 – 2 | 3 – 2 | 4 – 2 | 5 – 2 | 6 – 2 | 7 – 2 |
| 3 – 3 | 4 – 3 | 5 – 3 | 6 – 3 | 7 – 3 | 8 – 3 |
| 4 – 4 | 5 – 4 | 6 – 4 | 7 – 4 | 8 – 4 | 9 – 4 |
| 5 – 5 | 6 – 5 | 7 – 5 | 8 – 5 | 9 – 5 | 10 – 5 |
| 6 – 6 | 7 – 6 | 8 – 6 | 9 – 6 | 10 – 6 | 10 – 0 |
| 7 – 7 | 8 – 7 | 9 – 7 | 10 – 7 | 10 – 1 | 9 – 0 |
| 8 – 8 | 9 – 8 | 10 – 8 | 10 – 2 | 9 – 1 | 8 – 0 |
| 9 – 9 | 10 – 9 | 10 – 3 | 9 – 2 | 8 – 1 | 7 – 0 |
| 10 – 1 | 10 – 4 | 9 – 3 | 8 – 2 | 7 – 1 | 6 – 0 |

*Classworks* © Classworks Numeracy author team, Nelson Thornes Ltd, 2003

# Addition and Subtraction (3)

**Outcome**

*Children will be able to use number tracks and knowledge of number facts to solve additions and subtractions*

**Medium-term plan objectives**

- Understand the operations of addition and of subtraction and use the related vocabulary.
- Identify near doubles, using doubles already known.

**Overview**

- Addition using jumps on a number track.
- Subtraction on a number track by counting forward then back.
- Near addition doubles.

## How you could plan this unit

| | Stage 1 | Stage 2 | Stage 3 | Stage 4 | Stage 5 |
|---|---|---|---|---|---|
| **Content and vocabulary** | Working out additions by jumping on a number track and counting all | Working out subtractions by jumping forward and backward on a number track | Making families of near addition doubles and working out the answers | | |
| | *number track, addition, jumps* | *number track, subtraction, jumping back* | *near addition double, family, plus, minus* | | |
| **Notes** | Resource page A | Resource page B | | | |

57

# Working out additions by jumping on a number track and counting all

**Advance Organiser**

We are going to use a number track for adding numbers

**Oral/mental starter pp 181–182**

**You will need:** 0 to 20 number track (enlarged), resource page A (one per child)

## Whole-class work

- Show the children an enlarged 0 to 20 number track. Together count up from 0 to 20 as you point to each number.

- Tell them that a number track is a very good way of finding the answer to an addition.

- Write on the board: *5 + 4.*

- *How can the number track help find the answer to this addition?*

- If no one suggests it, show them that they must start at zero, then make 5 jumps followed by 4 jumps. Draw this above the number track. Use different colours for jumping 5 and for jumping 4.

| 0 | 1 | 2 | 3 | 4 | 5 | 6 | 7 | 8 | 9 | 10 | 11 | 12 | 13 | 14 | 15 | 16 | 17 | 18 | 19 | 20 |
|---|---|---|---|---|---|---|---|---|---|----|----|----|----|----|----|----|----|----|----|----|

- *Who can tell me what I have done?*

- *What is the answer to 5 + 4?*

- *Where on the number track does it show this?*

- Stress that the answer is the number at which the last jump ends.

- Repeat with 6 + 2.

## Independent, paired or group work

- Give each child a copy of resource page A. Show them how to draw the jumps for question 1 on the number track and where to write the answer.

- Ask them to do the rest of the questions.

## Plenary

- Invite the children to describe how they used the number track to find the answers to questions on resource page A.

- Remind them that the answer is shown by the number on which the last jump ends.

Name: _____

# Jump to add

Draw jumps to find the answer.

4 + 2 = ☐

| 0 | 1 | 2 | 3 | 4 | 5 | 6 | 7 | 8 | 9 | 10 |

2 + 6 = ☐

| 0 | 1 | 2 | 3 | 4 | 5 | 6 | 7 | 8 | 9 | 10 |

8 + 2 = ☐

| 0 | 1 | 2 | 3 | 4 | 5 | 6 | 7 | 8 | 9 | 10 |

3 + 5 = ☐

| 0 | 1 | 2 | 3 | 4 | 5 | 6 | 7 | 8 | 9 | 10 |

6 + 4 = ☐

| 0 | 1 | 2 | 3 | 4 | 5 | 6 | 7 | 8 | 9 | 10 |

# Working out subtractions by jumping forward and backward on a number track

**Advance Organiser**

We are going to use a number track for subtracting numbers

**Oral/mental starter pp 181–182**

**You will need:** 0 to 20 number track (enlarged), resource page B (one per child)

## Whole-class work

- Show the children an enlarged number track. Together count up from 0 to 20 as you point to each number.

- Tell them that they are going to use a number track to find the answer to subtractions.

- Write on the board: *8 – 3*.

- *How can the number track help find the answer to this subtraction?*

- Show them that they must start at 0, then make 8 jumps forward followed by 3 jumps back. Draw the forward jumps above the number track and the backward jumps below the track. Use different colours for jumping forward 8 and for jumping back 3.

| 0 | 1 | 2 | 3 | 4 | 5 | 6 | 7 | 8 | 9 | 10 | 11 | 12 | 13 | 14 | 15 | 16 | 17 | 18 | 19 | 20 |

- *Who can tell me what I have done?*

- *What is the answer to 8 – 3?*

- *Where on the number track does it show this?*

- Stress that the answer is the number at which the last jump coming back ends.

- Repeat with 7 – 5.

## Independent, paired or group work

- Give each child a copy of resource page B.

- Show them how to draw the jumps for question 1 on the number track and where to write the answer.

- Ask them to do the rest of the questions.

## Plenary

- Invite the children to describe how they used the number track to find the answers to questions on resource page B.

- Remind them that the answer is shown by the number at which the last jump coming back ends.

Name: _____

# Jumping back

Draw jumps to find the answer.

5 − 2 = ☐

| 0 | 1 | 2 | 3 | 4 | 5 | 6 | 7 | 8 | 9 | 10 |

9 − 4 = ☐

| 0 | 1 | 2 | 3 | 4 | 5 | 6 | 7 | 8 | 9 | 10 |

7 − 6 = ☐

| 0 | 1 | 2 | 3 | 4 | 5 | 6 | 7 | 8 | 9 | 10 |

8 − 3 = ☐

| 0 | 1 | 2 | 3 | 4 | 5 | 6 | 7 | 8 | 9 | 10 |

6 − 5 = ☐

| 0 | 1 | 2 | 3 | 4 | 5 | 6 | 7 | 8 | 9 | 10 |

*Classworks* © Classworks Numeracy author team, Nelson Thornes Ltd, 2003

# *Making families of near addition doubles and working out the answers*

Oral/mental starter pp 181–182

**Advance Organiser**

We are going to look for families of near addition doubles

## Whole-class work

- Write on the board the addition doubles: *1 + 1, 2 + 2, 3 + 3, 4 + 4* and *5 + 5.*
- *What is special about each of these additions?*
- Remind them that they are called addition doubles.
- *Why are they called addition doubles?*
- Ask for the answer to each and how they worked it out.
- Draw the diagram below and write *4 + 4* in the centre box.
- *I am making a family of additions. Tell me why they make a family – what is similar about them?*
- Write into the other boxes of the family diagram *4 + 3, 3 + 4, 5 + 4* and *4 + 5.*
- Tell the children that the family is called the *Near addition double family of 4 + 4.*
- *Why do you think it is called a near addition double family?*
- Explain that we can find the answer to each addition in the family by using the answer to the addition double.
- *What is the answer to 4 + 4?* Record on the board: *4 + 4 = 8.*
- Explain that 4 + 5 is 1 more than 4 + 4. *Explain to me why this is.*
- Record: *4 + 5 = double 4 plus 1 = 8 + 1 = 9.*
- Do the same for 5 + 4.
- Explain that 4 + 3 is 1 less than double 4. *Explain to me why this is.*
- Record: *4 + 3 = double 4 minus 1 = 8 – 1 = 7.*
- Do the same for 3 + 4.

Family diagram:
| 4 + 3 | 3 + 4 |
| 4 + 4 |
| 5 + 4 | 4 + 5 |

## Independent, paired or group work

- Children should draw their own diagrams for the near addition double families of 1 + 1 to 5 + 5 and record the relevant number facts.

## Plenary

- Invite the children to describe and explain what they did.
- Draw their attention to the fact that some near addition doubles belong in more than one family.
- Show them that 5 + 4 = double 4 plus 1 = 9 and 5 + 4 = double 5 minus 1 = 9.
- Ask them for other near addition doubles that are in more than one family and to find the answers.

# Addition and Subtraction (4)

**Outcome**

*Children will be able to use objects and number tracks to aid addition and subtraction, and record and explain their work*

**Medium-term plan objectives**

- Understand operation of addition, and of subtraction (as *how many more*).
- Partition into '5 and a bit' when adding 6, 7, 8, or 9.
- Bridge through 10 when adding single-digit numbers.

**Overview**

- Counting on, using a number track.
- Subtraction as how many more.
- Using physical apparatus to model bridging 10.

## How you could plan this unit

| | Stage 1 | Stage 2 | Stage 3 | Stage 4 | Stage 5 |
|---|---|---|---|---|---|
| **Content and vocabulary** | Using a number track to illustrate counting on from the first number when adding | Matching objects in two sets one-to-one to find how many more and recording as a subtraction | Using sets of cubes to change an addition of single digits to 10 + ? | | |
| | *number track, count on, from the first number* | *match, one-to-one, ring, how many more, subtraction* | *single-digit number, make into 10* | | |
| **Notes** | Resource page A | Resource pages B and C | Resource pages D and E | | |

# Using a number track to illustrate counting on from the first number when adding

**Advance Organiser**

We are going to learn about counting on to add two numbers

Oral/mental starter pp 181–182

**You will need:** 0 to 20 number track (enlarged), resource page A (one per child)

## Whole-class work

- Show the children the 0 to 20 number track.

- Write on the board the addition 9 + 6.

- *How can the number track help us find the answer to 9 + 6?*

- Above the track draw a jump of 9 followed by a jump of 6.

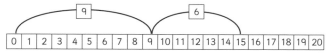

- Some children will need to see the large jumps broken up into single jumps; for example, 9 seen as nine jumps of 1.

- *What is the answer to 9 + 6?*

- It is important to make the distinction between numbers that show positions on the number track and numbers that indicate quantity, the size of a jump.

- Repeat for the additions 6 + 8, 8 + 7.

- Use the last example to show that the first jump ends on the same number as the size of the jump. Colour in the number. Use a different colour for the answer.

- Explain that this means we can omit the first jump and start the second jump at the first jump's number.

- Use this method for 7 + 4 and 13 + 6. When the second number is large, counting on in ones from the first number may be better for some children.

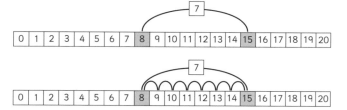

## Independent, paired or group work

- Ask the children to complete resource page A.

## Plenary

- Invite the children to show how they worked out the answers to the questions on resource page A. Each time, stress that it is not necessary to count the first jump, but to count on to find the answer.

- End with some oral additions counting on from the first number.

Name: _____

## Count on

| 0 | 1 | 2 | 3 | 4 | 5 | 6 | 7 | 8 | 9 | 10 | 11 | 12 | 13 | 14 | 15 | 16 | 17 | 18 | 19 | 20 |

| 0 | 1 | 2 | 3 | 4 | 5 | 6 | 7 | 8 | 9 | 10 | 11 | 12 | 13 | 14 | 15 | 16 | 17 | 18 | 19 | 20 |

| 0 | 1 | 2 | 3 | 4 | 5 | 6 | 7 | 8 | 9 | 10 | 11 | 12 | 13 | 14 | 15 | 16 | 17 | 18 | 19 | 20 |

| 0 | 1 | 2 | 3 | 4 | 5 | 6 | 7 | 8 | 9 | 10 | 11 | 12 | 13 | 14 | 15 | 16 | 17 | 18 | 19 | 20 |

| 0 | 1 | 2 | 3 | 4 | 5 | 6 | 7 | 8 | 9 | 10 | 11 | 12 | 13 | 14 | 15 | 16 | 17 | 18 | 19 | 20 |

7 + 9 = ☐

8 + 5 = ☐

7 + 6 = ☐

12 + 4 = ☐

16 + 3 = ☐

# Matching objects in two sets one-to-one to find how many more and recording as a subtraction

**Advance Organiser**

We are going to find out how many more

Oral/mental starter
pp 181–182

**You will need:** resource page B (enlarged), resource page C (one per child)

## Whole-class work

- Use an enlarged version of resource page B.

- Point to each set of cows in turn.

- *How many cows are in this field?*

- Match the cows one-to-one.

- *Who can tell me what I have done?*

- *How many more cows are there in this field than in this?*

- *How many more is 8 than 3?*

- Write on the board: *8 is more than 3 by 5.*

- Ring the matched cows in the larger set.

- *How many cows have I ringed?*

- *How many cows are left when 3 is taken away from 8?*

- Record on the board: *8 − 3 = 5.*

- Compare the two sentences on the board.

- Explain that 'how many more than' can be found by taking away.

- Repeat the activity with the sheep on the bottom half of resource page B.

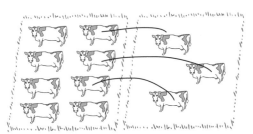

## Independent, paired or group work

- Work through the first question on resource page C together.

- Children match one-to-one, ring the matched objects in the larger set and then complete the subtraction.

## Plenary

- Ask mental questions such as *How many more is 7 than 5?*

- Ask a child to tell you how this can be written as a subtraction.

- Record each one on the board.

EXAMPLE

# Match the animals

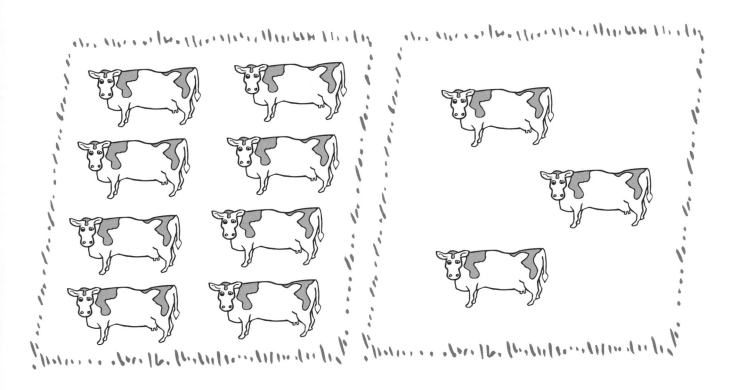

( PUPIL PAGE )

Name: _____

# How many more?

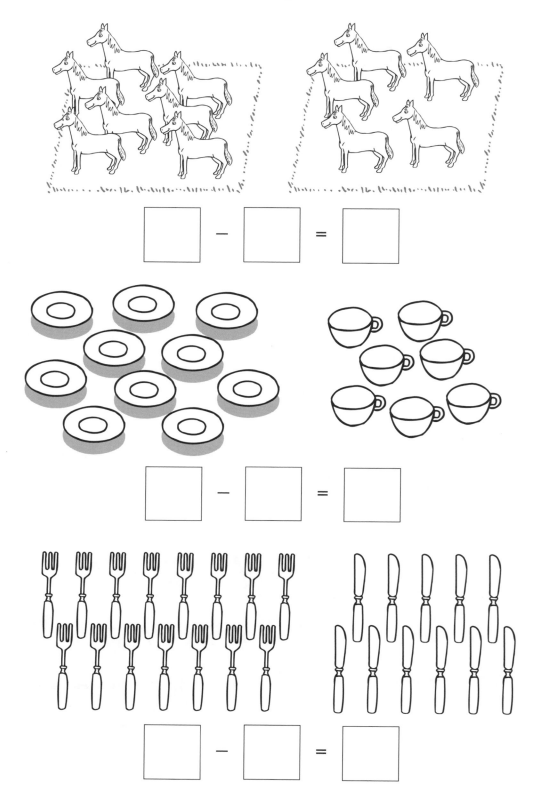

# Using sets of cubes to change an addition of single digits to 10 + ?

**Advance Organiser**

We are going to add single digit numbers with answers more than 10

Oral/mental starter pp 181–182

**You will need:** cubes, two sets of 0 to 9 number cards, set enclosures and cubes per child, resource page D (enlarged: one per pair), resource page E (one per child)

## Whole-class work

- Show a set of 8 cubes and a set of 6 cubes in a different colour.

- Together, count how many are in each set.

- *How many cubes are there altogether? How did you find out?*

- Move 2 cubes from the set of 6 to the set of 8 to make sets of 10 and 4. Explain at each stage what you are doing and why.

- *How many cubes in this set? How many cubes altogether?*

- Point out that they do not need to count every cube as there are 10 in one set and 10 and 4 make 14.

- Repeat with different single-digit numbers.

- Model 8 + 6 using this diagram.

- Make sure that the children understand the relationship between the actions with the cubes and the recording.

- *What is 10 + 4?*

- What is 8 + 6?

- *Which is easier, 10 + 4 or 8 + 6? Why?*

- Repeat for other additions of single-digit numbers.

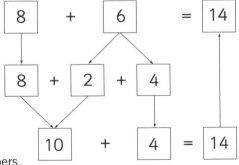

## Independent, paired or group work

- Each pair uses cubes and set enclosures to show the first example on resource page D.

- Together, repeat the actions of the first section of the whole-class work.

- One child in the pair then sets out the next example. The other child changes the sets so that they become 10 + ?.

- Individual children complete resource page E.

## Plenary

- Ask mental single-digit addition questions. Each time, record on the board how the question can be changed to make into a 10 + ? question.

**PUPIL PAGE**

Name: _____

# Make 10

9 and 8

6 and 9

9 and 4

3 and 8

7 and 8

( **PUPIL PAGE** )

Name: _____

# 10 + ?

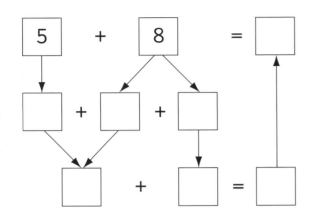

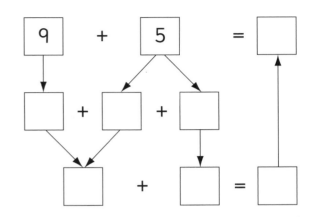

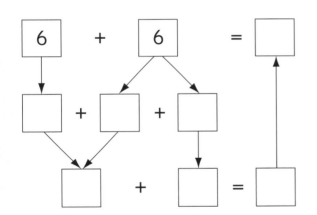

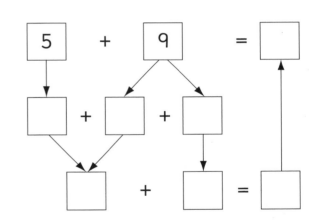

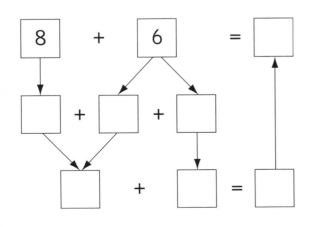

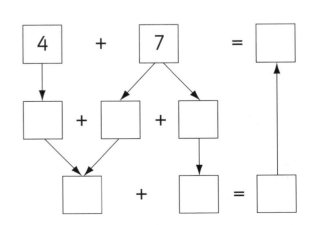

# Addition and Subtraction (5)

**Outcome**

*Children will be able to find possible additions and subtractions to make given answers*

| **Medium-term plan objectives** | • Use the +, – and = signs to record mental calculations in a number sentence.<br><br>• Recognise the use of □ and △ to stand for an unknown number.<br><br>• Use number facts to add or subtract pairs of numbers in the range 0 to 10. |
|---|---|
| **Overview** | • Recording addition and subtraction calculations as number sentences.<br><br>• Making additions to match an answer.<br><br>• Making subtractions to match an answer. |

## How you could plan this unit

| | Stage 1 | Stage 2 | Stage 3 | Stage 4 | Stage 5 |
|---|---|---|---|---|---|
| **Content and vocabulary** | Using the +, – and = signs to complete incomplete calculations<br><br>*incomplete calculations, =, – and = signs* | Finding additions for each of the answers 0 to 10 | Finding subtractions for each of the answers 0 to 10 | | |
| **Notes** | Resource page A | Resource page B | Resource page B | | |

# Using the +, – and = signs to complete incomplete calculations

**Advance Organiser**

We are going to find out where to put the +, – and = signs in calculations

**Oral/mental starter**
**pp 181–182**

**You will need:** number cards 0 to 9, +, – and = sign cards, resource page A (one per child)

## Whole-class work

- Use the 2, 1 and 3 number cards to make an incomplete 'addition' on the board.

- Show the children the + and the = signs.

- Explain that they have fallen off the sheet. Ask a child to put them on for you in the correct places.

- Read together the complete addition.

- Repeat for a few more additions.

- Do the same for some subtractions.

- Use the numbers 7, 4 and 3 to make an incomplete calculation.

- Show the children the +, – and = signs.

- *I am not sure if this is an addition or a subtraction.*

- Give a child the three signs and ask them to complete the calculation.

- Note: it could be 7 – 4 = 3 OR 7 = 4 + 3.

- Whichever the child chooses, challenge the class to make the other calculation.

- Repeat for other calculations using the three signs.

## Independent, paired or group work

- Each child completes resource page A, writing in the missing signs.

## Plenary

- Ask the children in turn to show how they did some of the questions from resource page A.

- Where appropriate, show it is possible to have two solutions.

Name: _____

# Which sign?

| 1 | ◯ | 3 | ◯ | 4 |    | 5 | ◯ | 2 | ◯ | 7 |

| 8 | ◯ | 5 | ◯ | 3 |    | 3 | ◯ | 6 | ◯ | 9 |

| 7 | ◯ | 6 | ◯ | 1 |    | 9 | ◯ | 6 | ◯ | 3 |

| 8 | ◯ | 2 | ◯ | 6 |    | 4 | ◯ | 5 | ◯ | 9 |

| 2 | ◯ | 6 | ◯ | 8 |    | 6 | ◯ | 1 | ◯ | 5 |

| 7 | ◯ | 1 | ◯ | 8 |    | 4 | ◯ | 2 | ◯ | 2 |

# *Finding additions for each of the answers 0 to 10*

**Advance Organiser**

We are going to make up additions that have different answers

**Oral/mental starter pp 181–182**

You will need: resource page B (first half: 11 cards per child)

## Whole-class work

- Ask a child to tell you an addition that has an answer less than 11.

- Write the addition on the board.

- *What is the answer to this addition?*

- Ask a child to tell you another addition, but it must have a different answer to the one on the board and still be less than 11.

- *What is the answer to this addition?*

- Repeat this until there is an addition with every answer from 0 to 10.

$$2 + 4 = 6$$
$$1 + 7 = 8$$
$$5 + 5 = 10$$
$$1 + 0 = 1$$
$$7 + 2 = 9$$
$$4 + 1 = 5$$
$$1 + 1 = 2$$
$$3 + 1 = 4$$
$$2 + 5 = 7$$
$$0 + 0 = 0$$
$$2 + 1 = 3$$

## Independent, paired or group work

- Each child has 11 blank addition cards made from resource page B.

- They make up 11 additions, each with a different answer.

- When complete, they put them in order of the answers.

## Plenary

- Write across the board the answers 0, 1, 2, 3 and so on to 10 in a random order.

- Ask the children to give you an addition that has each of the answers. Do not write its answer.

- Where there is more than one addition, ask for others.

- Record each in its correct place.

- End by rubbing out the answers across the page.

- Point to additions in turn asking for the answer.

CUT-OUT

# Number fact cards

$\square + \square = \square$   $\square + \square = \square$

$\square + \square = \square$   $\square + \square = \square$

$\square + \square = \square$   $\square + \square = \square$

$\square - \square = \square$   $\square - \square = \square$

$\square - \square = \square$   $\square - \square = \square$

$\square - \square = \square$   $\square - \square = \square$

*Classworks* © Classworks Numeracy author team, Nelson Thornes Ltd, 2003

# Finding subtractions for each of the answers 0 to 10

**Advance Organiser**

We are going to make up subtractions that have different answers

**Oral/mental starter pp 181–182**

**You will need:** resource page B (second half: 11 cards per child)

**Whole-class work**

- Ask a child to tell you a subtraction that has an answer less than 11.

- Write the subtraction on the board.

- *What is the answer to this subtraction?*

- Ask a child to tell you another subtraction, but it must have a different answer to the one on the board and still be less than 11.

- *What is the answer to this subtraction?*

- Repeat this until there is a subtraction on the board with every answer from 0 to 10.

$$7 - 3 = 4$$
$$9 - 1 = 8$$
$$10 - 0 = 10$$
$$6 - 5 = 1$$
$$9 - 0 = 9$$
$$8 - 3 = 5$$
$$6 - 4 = 2$$
$$7 - 1 = 6$$
$$10 - 3 = 7$$
$$2 - 2 = 0$$
$$4 - 1 = 3$$

**Independent, paired or group work**

- Each child has 11 blank subtraction cards made from resource page B.

- They make up 11 subtractions, each with a different answer.

- When complete, they put them in order of the answers.

**Plenary**

- Write across the board the answers 0, 1, 2, 3 and so on to 10 in a random order.

- Ask the children to give you a subtraction that has each of the answers. Do not write its answer.

- Where there is more than one subtraction, ask for others.

- Record each in its correct place.

- End by rubbing out the answers across the page.

- Point to subtractions in turn asking for the answer.

# Addition and Subtraction (6)

**Outcome**

*Children will be able to use structured jottings to support and explain mental strategies for addition and subtraction*

**Medium-term plan objectives**

- Add more than two numbers.
- Use number facts to add or subtract pairs of numbers within the range 0 to 20.
- Add 9 to a single-digit number by adding 10 then subtracting 1.
- Bridging through 20 when adding a single-digit number.

**Overview**

- Count how many objects in three sets.
- Add three single-digit numbers of 6 or less.
- Make up an addition using numbers 10 or less and find its answer.
- Make up a subtraction using numbers 20 or less and find its answer.
- Add 9 by adding 10 and subtracting 1.
- Add a single digit to a 'teens' number crossing 20.

## How you could plan this unit

| | Stage 1 | Stage 2 | Stage 3 | Stage 4 | Stage 5 |
|---|---|---|---|---|---|
| **Content and vocabulary** | Count the totals of objects and numbers in the rows and columns of a 3-by-3 grid | Using the numbers 1 to 10 to make up five additions and finding the answers | Using the numbers 1 to 20 to make up ten subtractions and finding the answers | Using a diagram to show how to add 9 as 10 subtract 1 | Using a 1 to 30 number grid and a diagram to change the addition of a 'teens' and a single digit to 20 + ? |
| | *total, row, column* | *addition* | *subtraction* | *same answer as, make 9 into 10 subtract 1* | *make into 20* |
| **Notes** | Resource page A | | | Resource page B | Resource page C |

# *Count the totals of objects and numbers in the rows and columns of a 3-by-3 grid*

**Advance Organiser**

We are going to find the total of three single-digit numbers

Oral/mental starter
pp 181–182

**You will need:** linking cubes, 1 to 10 number cards, resource page A (one per child)

**Whole-class work**

- Place linking cube sticks as shown on the following diagram drawn on the board.

- In turn, point to each square.

- *How many cubes in this square?*

- Point to the three squares in the top row.

- *How many cubes altogether in these three squares?*

- Explain that the total number of cubes in the three squares is written in the circle at the end of the arrow. Write or put a 10 number card in the circle.

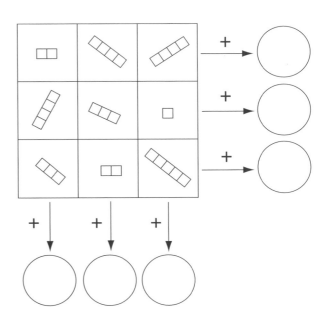

- Repeat for each of the other rows and columns.

- Remove all the totals. Rearrange the nine sticks into different squares.

- Repeat the questioning, but this time ask the children to place a number card for each of the totals.

**Independent, paired or group work**

- The children complete resource page A.

**Plenary**

- Check on the children's answers for resource page A.

- End with mental additions of three single-digit numbers such as 3 + 4 + 2.

Name: _____

# Rows and columns

Write the total number of cubes in each row and each column.

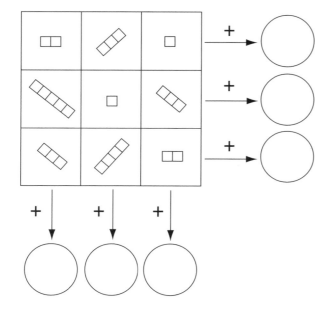

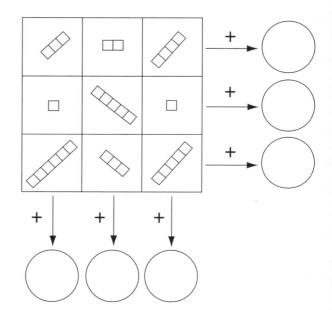

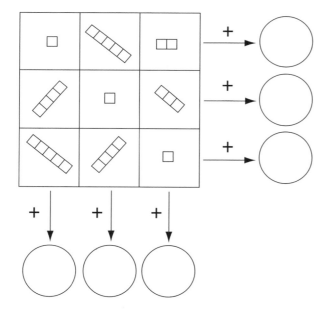

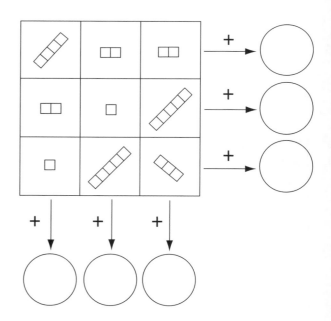

# Using the numbers 1 to 10 to make up five additions and finding the answers

**Advance Organiser**

We are going to make up additions using number cards

**Oral/mental starter pp 181–182**

**You will need:** number cards 1 to 10 and 1 to 20 (for you and per child)

## Whole-class work

- Ask the children in turn to choose two of the 1 to 10 number cards to make an addition.

- Record the addition on the board; for example, 8 + 4.

- *What is the answer to 8 + 4?*

- Use the 12 card from the second set to record the answer.

- Repeat until all the 1 to 10 cards have been used.

| 8 | + | 4 | = | 12 |
| 3 | + | 5 | = | 8 |
| | + | | = | |

- If an answer card has already been used, the pair of numbers should be changed.

- Remove the cards and answers and repeat the activity.

## Independent, paired or group work

- Each child uses the 1 to 10 number cards to make five additions. They then calculate the answers and place the appropriate 1 to 20 number card in each answer place. (They may need the same answer card more than once.)

- When complete, they record the five additions in their exercise book.

- Early finishers can repeat the activity.

## Plenary

- In turn, ask the children to tell you their additions. Record them on the board and ask other children for the answers.

# Using the numbers 1 to 20 to make up ten subtractions and finding the answers

**Advance Organiser**

We are going to make up and solve some subtractions

**Oral/mental starter pp 181–182**

**You will need:** number cards 1 to 20 (two sets for you and per child)

## Whole-class work

- Ask the children in turn to choose two of the first set of 1 to 20 number cards to make a subtraction.

- Record the subtraction on the board; for example, 15 – 3.

- *What is the answer to 15 – 3?*

- Use the 12 card from the second set to record the answer.

- Repeat until five subtractions have been made.

- Remove the cards.

- Repeat the activity with the remaining ten cards in the first set.

| 15 | – | 3 | = | 12 |
| --- | --- | --- | --- | --- |
| | – | | = | |
| | – | | = | |
| | – | | = | |
| | – | | = | |

## Independent, paired or group work

- Each child uses the first set of 1 to 20 number cards to make five subtractions. They then calculate the answers and place the appropriate number card from the second set in each answer place. (They may need the same answer card more than once.)

- When complete, they record the five subtractions in their exercise book.

- Early finishers use the remaining ten cards to make five more subtractions.

## Plenary

- In turn, ask the children to tell you their subtractions. Record them on the board and ask other children for the answers.

# Using a diagram to show how to add 9 as 10 subtract 1

**Advance Organiser**

We are going to see an easy way of adding 9 to any number

**Oral/mental starter pp 181–182**

**You will need:** number cards 2 to 9, resource page B (one per child)

**Whole-class work**

- Draw the following diagram for the children.
- Place 6 and 9 in the boxes on the top line.
- *What is the answer to 6 + 9?*
- Record it in the top right answer box.
- *Tell me how you did it.*
- *Who can tell me an easy way to add 9?*
- Put 10 and 1 in their boxes.
- *Why have I put 10 and 1 in these boxes instead of a 9?*
- Complete the second row with the 6.
- Tell the children again about how the numbers in the first row relate to the numbers in the second row and how the arrows help to show what has happened at each stage.
- In turn, point to each box in the last row.
- *What number goes in this box? How did you decide?*
- Put in the 16 and the 1.
- *We have changed 6 + 9 into 16 – 1 because they have the same answer.*
- Ask for the answer to 16 – 1. Record it.
- *Which is easier, 6 + 9 or 16 – 1? Why do you think that?*
- Repeat the activity with other single digit numbers.

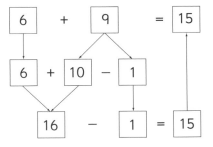

**Independent, paired or group work**

- Together, work through the first example on resource page B.
- Each child completes resource page B. You may need to help some children as the 10 and the 1 have been omitted from each diagram.

**Plenary**

- In turn, ask the children to explain how they did each question on resource page B.
- Write on the board: *9 = 10 – 1. Who can tell me what I have written?*
- Read out the number sentence in the form *Nine is the same value as ten take away one.*
- Make clear that the = symbol does not just mean 'find an answer', it represents a relationship.
- Clarify that the addition in the first row has the same answer as the subtraction in the last row.
- *Six plus nine equals fifteen. Six plus nine has the same value as fifteen. Sixteen take away one has the same value as fifteen.*

Name: _____

# Easy add 9

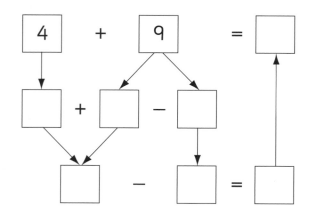

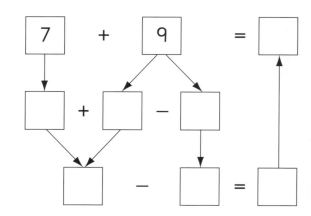

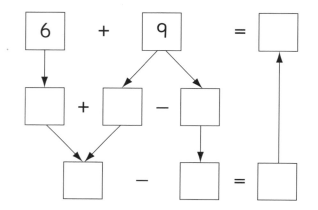

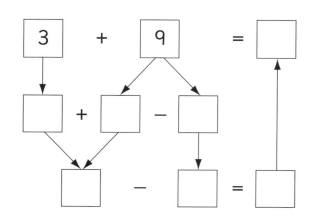

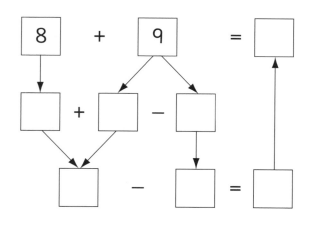

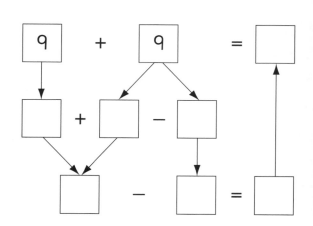

# Using a 1 to 30 number grid and a diagram to change the addition of a 'teens' and a single digit to 20 + ?

**Advance Organiser**

We are going to find out how to add single-digit numbers to teens numbers

**Oral/mental starter pp 181–182**

**You will need:** 1 to 30 number grid or track. resource page C (one per child)

## Whole-class work

- Write on the board: *17 + 5*.
- Show the children an enlarged 1 to 30 number grid or track.
- *How can we use this number grid to find the answer to 17 + 5?*
- Ask how many is needed to make the 17 into 20.
- Use the number grid to show that 3 more will do this by counting along the row from 17 to 20 with the class.
- *We can use 3 from the 5. How many of the 5 will be left?*
- Use the number grid to show that 17 + 5 has the same value as 17 + 3 + 2 and has an answer of 22.
- Repeat the activity with other 'teens' numbers bridging 20.
- Draw the outline of the diagram below on the board.
- Write 17 and 5 in the first row. Remind them that they have already found the answer to this addition using the number grid.
- Explain what the arrows mean and build up the rest of the diagram leaving out the two answers.
- At each stage question the children about what you are doing and why.
- Reinforce that 17 + 5 has the same value as 20 + 2.
- *What is the answer to 20 + 2?*
- *What is the answer to 17 + 5?*
- *Which addition is easier to do? Why do you think that?*

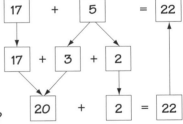

## Independent, paired or group work

- Each child completes resource page C. Work through the first question together.

## Plenary

- In turn, ask the children to show how they did a question on resource page C.
- Continually remind them that the 'teens' number is made up to 20 and the two additions have the same answer (are the same value as each other).

PUPIL PAGE

Name: _____

# Easy adding

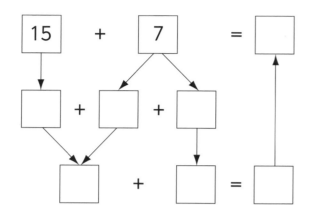

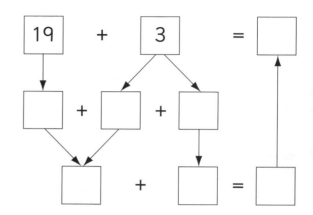

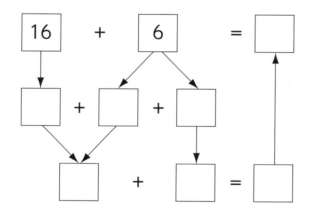

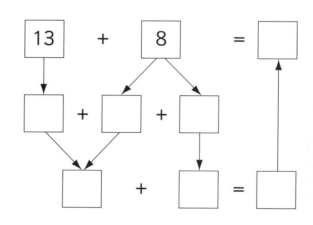

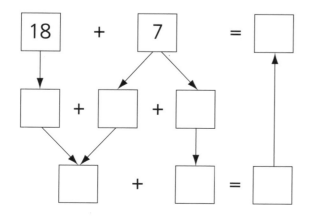

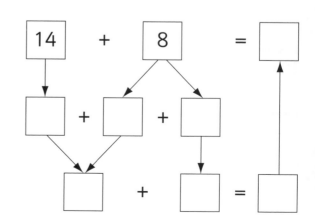

Classworks © Classworks Numeracy author team, Nelson Thornes Ltd, 2003

# *Solving Problems (1)*

**Outcome**

*Children will be able to find different ways of totalling 10p*

| **Medium-term plan objectives** | ● Recognise 1p and 2p coins. Find totals up to 10p. |
| | ● Choose and use the appropriate number operation and mental strategy to solve problems. |

| **Overview** | ● Totalling 1p and 2p coins. |
| | ● Finding sets of coins with the same total. |
| | ● Finding ways of counting. |
| | ● Finding different answers. |

## How you could plan this unit

| | Stage 1 | Stage 2 | Stage 3 | Stage 4 | Stage 5 |
|---|---|---|---|---|---|
| **Content and vocabulary** | Counting coins<br><br>*pence, pennies, coin, worth the same as, same value as* | Five coin totals<br><br>*greatest, smallest, worth, order, first* | | | |
| **Notes** | | | | | |

# *Counting coins*

Oral/mental starter
p 182

**Advance Organiser**

We are going to find lots of ways to add coins

**You will need:** 2p and 1p coins, Blu-Tack or sticky tape

## Whole-class work

- Draw two bags and label them *1p* and *2p*.

- Draw sets with blank labels beneath the bags as shown.

- *Which bag shall I choose a coin from?*

- Write or stick the coin in one of the sets. Repeat for a coin from the other bag.

- *How much money is in the 1p set? How much is in the 2p set?*

- Agree the totals of 1p and 2p respectively.

- *Now I am going to choose two coins for each of these sets.*

- *Which shall I choose?*

- Write or stick the chosen coins in the next row of sets.

- Repeat for other combinations.

- Each time, ask how much money altogether and write the total on the label.

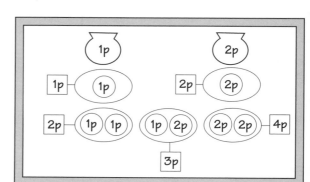

## Independent, paired or group work

- Ask the children to find different totals for sets of three coins.

- Tell them to use diagrams to record their work as on the board.

- More able children can explore combinations of more coins.

## Plenary

- Ask the children to talk about different totals they found and how they worked out each one.

- Invite the children to show different ways to make the same total.

- Draw a set of three 1p coins and one 2p coin on the board.

- Ask the children to find their total and agree it as a class.

- Draw them underneath in a different order.

- Ask the children to find the total again.

- *What do you notice?*

# *Five coin totals*

**Advance Organiser**

We are going to find different totals using five coins

Oral/mental starter
p 182

**You will need:** 1p and 2p coins, Blu-Tack or sticky tape

## Whole-class work

- Draw five squares on the board.

- *We are going to put a 1p or 2p coin in each square.*

- Place five 1p coins in the squares.

- *How much money is this worth altogether?*

- Record each coin in the number addition shown and complete the answer with the children.

- Repeat with four 1p coins and a 2p coin.

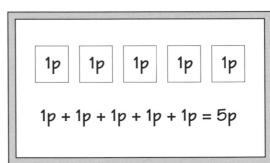

## Independent, paired or group work

- Ask the children to record different totals for five coins in the same way.

- Give them coins to work with.

- More able children can work with more 2p coins.

## Plenary

- *Which set of five coins is worth the most money?*

- *How do you know?*

- Repeat for the smallest amount of money.

- Ask the children to help you to find all the totals starting with the smallest (five 1p coins).

- Return to the smallest total and replace a 1p coin with a 2p coin.

- *What will the total be now?*

- *How do you know?*

- Repeat until all the 1p coins have been replaced by 2p coins.

# Solving Problems (2)

**Outcome**

*Children will be able to use counting on and back to solve simple problems*

| | |
|---|---|
| **Medium-term plan objectives** | • Choose and use the appropriate number operation (*counting*, *add*, *subtract*) and mental strategies to solve simple problems. |
| **Overview** | • Using a picture to solve a problem.<br>• Using counting forward and back.<br>• Organising work carefully.<br>• Using trial and improvement.<br>• Making decisions. |

## How you could plan this unit

| | Stage 1 | Stage 2 | Stage 3 | Stage 4 | Stage 5 |
|---|---|---|---|---|---|
| **Content and vocabulary** | Forward, back and forward<br><br>*count on, add, count back, subtract, order, first, second, third/last* | Crossing the river<br><br>*count on, add, count back, subtract, order* | | | |
| **Notes** | Resource page A | Resource page B | | | |

# *Forward, back and forward*

Oral/mental starter
p 182

**Advance Organiser**

We are going to move forward and back along a number track

**You will need:** toy person or animal, coloured pencils, felt pens, chalk, resource page A (one enlarged and one per child), 0 to 10 number track (enlarged)

## Whole-class work

- Place the toy at the start of the diagram of the stepping stones on resource page A.
- *The toy jumps forward then back and then forward again.*
- Move the toy forward six jumps, back two jumps and forward six jumps.
- Count each sequence of jumps and pause after finishing each movement so that the children can see where the toy has landed each time.
- Point out the stone that the toy finishes on.
- *How many stones has the toy moved away from the land?*
- Count out the stones with the class (10).
- Draw lines to show the jumps on a number track.
- Point out that *10* is the end of the jumps.
- Record the jumps on the table on resource page A in the form *forward 6, back 2, forward 6*.
- Repeat for other jumps; for example, forward five, back two, forward three.
- Ask a child to move the toy along the stones as you read out the instruction.

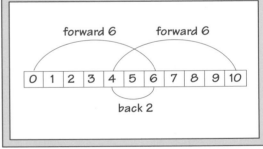

- *How many stones away from the land is the toy now?* (6)
- Draw the jumps on a number track to check.
- Record the sequence of jumps each time.

## Independent, paired or group work

- Ask the children to complete resource page A.
- They have to colour the stone landed on each time in a different colour.
- Early finishers could be asked to explore using four jumps.

## Plenary

- Invite the children to show some of their solutions.
- Ask the class to help you work out the number of the stone they have coloured each time.
- Write the numbers on the stones with the help of the children.
- Write the numbers on the intervening stones with the help of the children.
- Show examples of clear recording using the tables.

Name: _____

# Forward, back and forward

Colour the stone that each toy finishes on.

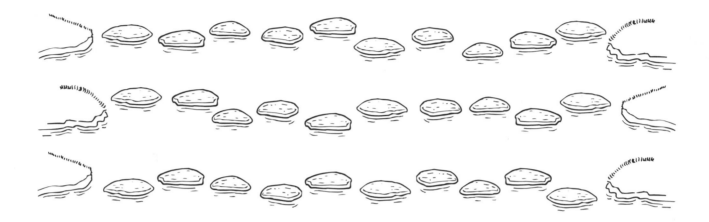

Kangaroo says 'I jumped forward 2, back 1 and forward 3.'

Frog says 'I jumped forward 4, back 2 and forward 5.'

Teddy says 'I jumped forward 5, back 4 and forward 7.'

| first jump | second jump | third jump |
|---|---|---|
|  |  |  |
|  |  |  |
|  |  |  |
|  |  |  |

# Crossing the river

**Advance Organiser**

We are going to decide how to land on 10 by counting on and back

**Oral/mental starter p 182**

**You will need:** toy person or animal, coloured pencils, resource page B (one enlarged and one per child), 0 to 10 number track

## Whole-class work

- Show the children an enlarged version of resource page B.

- *The toy starts at 0 and wants to get across the river to 10.*

- *How many jumps is that?*

- *We will have to move ten jumps to cross the river.*

- *The toy has to jump forward, then back, then forward.*

- *Who can help the toy get across the river?*

- *What could my first jump be? What about my second jump?*

- *The toy jumps forward five. Who can help me move the toy forward five?*

- *Now the toy has to jump back two.*

- *How far does the toy need to jump now to land on 10 exactly?*

- Take suggestions from the children and try some out.

- Draw the jumps on a number track.

- Record the jumps on the table on resource page B as *forward 5, back 2, forward 7*.

- Try other suggestions of jumps, illustrating them on a number line each time.

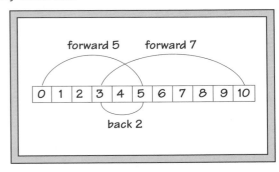

## Independent, paired or group work

- Ask the children to complete resource page B.

- They should record as many combinations of jumps as possible to get to 10 exactly.

- Early finishers could make a set of four jumps to end on 10.

## Plenary

- Invite the children to show their solutions.

- Encourage them to explain how they decided on their jumps.

- Demonstrate using different coloured lines and marking jumps above and below the stepping stones.

**PUPIL PAGE**

Name: _____

# Crossing the river

| first jump | second jump | third jump |
|---|---|---|
|  |  |  |
|  |  |  |
|  |  |  |
|  |  |  |
|  |  |  |
|  |  |  |
|  |  |  |
|  |  |  |

# *Solving Problems (3)*

**Outcome**

*Children will be able to explore making the same total with different sets of coins*

**Medium-term plan objectives**

- Recognise 1p, 2p, 5p and 10p coins and equivalent values. Find totals.
- Choose and use the appropriate number operation and mental strategy to solve problems.

**Overview**

- Count money.
- Find different answers.
- Find 'hidden coins'.
- Use trial and improvement to find the answer.

## How you could plan this unit

| | Stage 1 | Stage 2 | Stage 3 | Stage 4 | Stage 5 |
|---|---|---|---|---|---|
| **Content and vocabulary** | Money banks<br><br>*value, worth, is the same as, equals* | Hidden coins<br><br>*value, worth, is the same as, equals* | | | |
| **Notes** | | | | | |

# Money banks

**Advance Organiser**

We are going to add coins to make 17p in different ways

Oral/mental starter
p 182

**You will need:** 1p coin per child, several 2p, 5p and 10p coins, Blu-Tack or sticky tape

## Whole-class work

- Draw two money boxes and write 6p on a tag on each.

- *What coins could we put in this money box to make 6p?*

- Draw or stick the coins in place as they are suggested.

- *Can we use a different set of coins to make 6p in this money box?*

- Draw or stick the coins in place.

- Demonstrate that both sets of coins are worth the same.

- *Who can add 5p and 1p for me?*

- *What about 2p and 2p and 2p?*

- Write the matching sums on the board.

- Repeat for totals of 9p and 11p.

$$5p + 1p = 6p$$

$$2p + 2p + 2p = 6p$$

## Independent, paired or group work

- Ask the children to repeat the exercise for a total of 17p, recording the addition each time.

- Early finishers can choose their own totals and record different ways of making them.

## Plenary

- Invite the children to show their solutions.

- *Did anyone make that total in a different way?*

- Use a drawing to show that re-arranging the order of the coins does not make a different set; for example, 5p and 2p and 2p has the same value as 2p and 5p and 2p.

# *Hidden coins*

**Advance Organiser**
We are going to find out which three coins make 12p

**Oral/mental starter**
**p 182**

**You will need:** 1p, 2p, 5p and 10p coins for each group of children, Blu-Tack or sticky tape

## Whole-class work

- Draw a money box with a blank tag.

- Draw three squares big enough to hold 2p coins in the money box and write 9p on the tag.

- *There are three coins in the money box.*

- *What three coins could they be to add to 9p?*

- Use trial-and-improvement methods to find the value of the coins in the money box.

- Record all the attempts beneath the money box.

- Repeat for three coins used to make 16p.

10p + 2p + 2p = 14p (not 9p)

10p + 2p + 1p = 13p (not 9p)

5p + 2p + 2p = 9p ✓

## Independent, paired or group work

- Ask the children to repeat the exercise for totals of 12p and 22p, recording their work each time.

- Early finishers can decide their own totals to find.

## Plenary

- Invite the children to show their solutions.

- Show examples of clear records of trial-and-improvement.

- Work through a trial-and-improvement example.

- *3 coins are worth 14p*

- *10p 10p 10p = 30p. This total is too large. We need to use coins that are worth less money.*

- *10p 5p 5p = 20p. Still too large.*

- *10p 2p 2p = 14p. Correct.*

# Solving Problems (4)

**Outcome**

*Children will be able to give change from 20p*

| | |
|---|---|
| **Medium-term plan objectives** | • Find totals, give change. |
| | • Work out how to pay an amount by using smaller coins. |
| | • Solve simple mathematical problems or puzzles. |
| | • Explain methods orally. |
| | • Choose and use the appropriate number operation and mental strategy to solve a problem. |
| **Overview** | • Give change from 20p. |
| | • Find different ways to give change. |
| | • Know that some answers cannot be made. |
| | • Say why some answers cannot be made. |
| | • Solve word problems using diagrams. |
| | • Apply missing-number puzzles to word problems. |

## How you could plan this unit

| | Stage 1 | Stage 2 | Stage 3 | Stage 4 | Stage 5 |
|---|---|---|---|---|---|
| **Content and vocabulary** | Change (one coin)<br><br>*price, cost, change, money, coin, pence, pennies* | Change (more than one coin) | What did it cost? | | |
| **Notes** | Resource pages A and B | | Resource page C | | |

# Change (one coin)

**Advance Organiser**

We are going to work out how much change

**Oral/mental starter**
**p 182**

**You will need:** 1p, 2p, 5p and 10p coins, resource page A (per child), resource page B (enlarged)

## Whole-class work

- Show the children an enlarged version of resource page B and write 4p under the pencil.

- *This pencil costs 4p. I give the shopkeeper a 5p coin.*

- *How much change should I get?*

- Take suggestions from the children.

- Point out, if necessary, that one 5p coin is the same as five 1p coins.

- *If I give the shopkeeper five 1p coins, what change will I get if the pencil costs 4p?*

- *So, if I give the shopkeeper one 5p coin, what change will I get if the pencil costs 4p?*

- Illustrate this on the board by drawing 'coins' to represent 5p, then taking away four of them to leave 1p change.

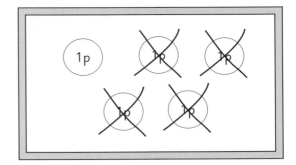

- Write underneath *5p take away 4p leaves 1p* and *5p – 4p = 1p*.

- Repeat for other single coin change activities, such as 5p – 3p = 2p, 2p – 1p = 1p and 10p – 5p = 5p.

## Independent, paired or group work

- Ask the children to complete resource page A.

## Plenary

- Invite the children to share their work.

- Show the children that it is easier to count sets of change starting with the largest coins, for example, 5p add 2p add 2p add 1p rather than 2p add 1p add 5p add 2p.

- Show the children how shopkeepers might count out change, for example, count from 10p to 20p placing 2p coins in a partner's hand: 10p, 12p, 14p, 16p, 18p, 20p.

- Repeat with sets of identical coins; for example, 10p to 20p using 5p coins.

Name: _____

# Giving change with one coin

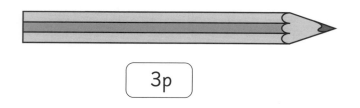

3p

Write how much change from 5p.

_____

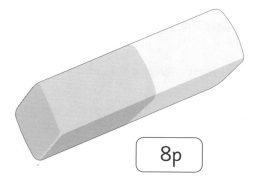

8p

Write how much change from 10p.

_____

5p

Write how much change from 10p.

_____

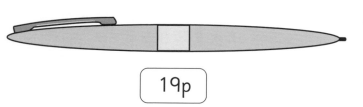

19p

Write how much change from 20p.

_____

Name: _____

# Giving change with one coin

Write how much change

from [     ] p.

_____

Write how much change

from [     ] p.

_____

Write how much change

from [     ] p.

_____

Write how much change

from [     ] p.

_____

*Classworks* © Classworks Numeracy author team, Nelson Thornes Ltd, 2003

# Change (more than one coin)

Oral/mental starter
p 182

**Advance Organiser**

We are going to work out how much change

**You will need:** 1p, 2p, 5p and 10p coins

## Whole-class work

- Draw some 'purses' on the board containing, respectively, one unmarked coin, two unmarked coins, three unmarked coins and four unmarked coins.

- *Rubia had 2p and spent 1p.*

- *Which of these purses could be her change?*

- *Could these two coins be her change?*

- *What about these three coins? Why not?*

- Confirm that the answer must be a single coin.

- *The change from 2p is 1p. We can only make 1p using one coin.*

- Repeat for Lemar. He had 10p and spent 8p.

- *Could the change be two coins? Could it be one coin?*

- Record this on the board as one 2p coin and underneath it two 1p coins.

- Repeat for various amounts, challenging children to think of the different ways to make each amount of change.

- Record each arrangement.

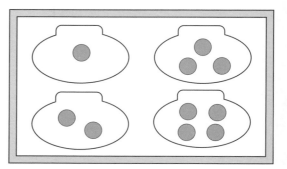

## Independent, paired or group work

- Give the children the following problems: *Jill had 20p. She spent 10p*; *Dave had 20p. He spent 6p*; *Beth had 20p. She spent 11p*; *Rob had 20p. He spent 9p.*

- They have to work out which combinations of one to four coins could make each amount of change and record each combination.

## Plenary

- Invite the children to show their answers.

- *Why couldn't Jill have been given three coins as change?*

- *Why can't you make 9p with two coins?*

- *Which amounts of money can't be made with one coin? Why?*

- Investigate various ways of making totals. Compare the children's answers.

# What did it cost?

**Advance Organiser**

We are going to find out how much the comic cost by looking at the change we got back

**Oral/mental starter p 182**

**You will need:** 1p, 2p, 5p and 10p coins, Blu-Tack or sticky tape, resource page C (enlarged)

## Whole-class work

- *I had 8p.*
- *I was given 2p change when I bought a comic.*
- *How much did the comic cost?*
- Ask the children to brainstorm some ways of finding out.
- Show the children an enlarged version of resource page C.
- In the 'I had' box write 8p.
- In the 'Change' box write 2p.
- *How can this help us to solve the problem?*
- Encourage the children towards the idea that the price and the change must add up to the amount you had in the first place.
- *I start with 8p. I take some money away. I have 2p left.*
- Write various ways of expressing this on the board.
- Solve the problem and check with one of the above calculations.
- Repeat with 5p as the change.
- Repeat, starting with 10p and getting 3p change.

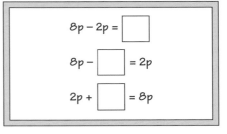

$$8p - 2p = \boxed{\phantom{x}}$$

$$8p - \boxed{\phantom{x}} = 2p$$

$$2p + \boxed{\phantom{x}} = 8p$$

## Independent, paired or group work

- Ask the children to find the price of an item giving: 3p change from 9p; 4p change from 13p; 6p change from 18p; 13p change from 17p.

## Plenary

- Invite the children to show their answers.
- Discuss some of the answers.
- Go over another example, stressing that the cost of the item and the change must add up to the original amount of money.
- Practise and write some inverse calculations with the class in this format.
- *I have 11p. I take away some money. I have 6p left.*
- *11p take away* what *makes 6p?*
- Write on the board $11p - \boxed{\phantom{x}} = 6p$.
- *What added to 6p makes 11p?*
- Write on the board $6p + \boxed{\phantom{x}} = 11p$.
- *11p take away 6p makes* what?
- Write on the board $11p - 6p = \boxed{\phantom{x}}$.
- Solve the three equations and point out that if you can answer one, you can answer all of them.

## What did it cost?

Name: _____

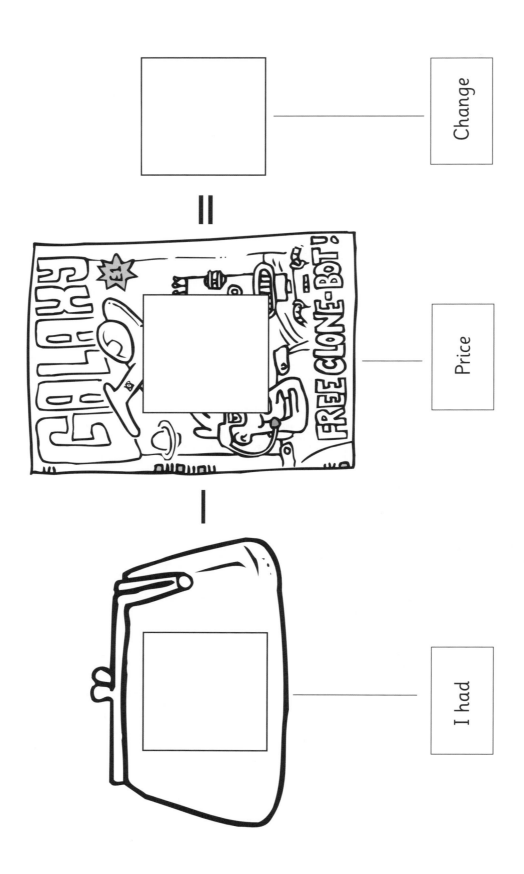

Change

Price

I had

# Solving Problems (5)

**Outcome**

*Children will be able to find different solutions to problems involving coins*

**Medium-term plan objectives**

- Recognise coins of different values up to 20p.
- Find totals, give change from up to 20p and work out how to pay using smaller coins.
- Choose and use the appropriate number operation and mental strategy to solve problems.

**Overview**

- Find pairs and sets of coins to make totals.
- Find different ways to solve puzzles.
- Extend a method to solve a more complex problem.

## How you could plan this unit

| | Stage 1 | Stage 2 | Stage 3 | Stage 4 | Stage 5 |
|---|---|---|---|---|---|
| **Content and vocabulary** | Coin puzzles<br><br>*penny, pence, coins, value, total, amount* | Two-coin puzzles | Nine coins | | |
| **Notes** | Resource page A | Resource page B | Resource page C | | |

# Coin puzzles

Oral/mental starter
p 182

**Advance Organiser**

We are going to find different ways to solve coin problems

**You will need:** 1p, 2p, 5p, 10p and 20p coins, resource page A

## Whole-class work

- Draw the following diagram on the board.

- Write a coin value in each box but leave the totals empty.

- *Who can tell me about this puzzle? Can anyone see what we have to do?*

- Encourage the children towards the idea of totalling the coins in rows and columns.

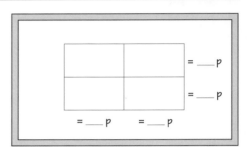

- Point out the equals signs to lead children towards this conclusion.

- *Who can help me add these coins across? How did you do that?*

- Ask for different ideas of how to add the coins. Write the totals.

- Encourage a range of responses including counting on, number bonds and so on.

- Rub out the coins and ask the children to help you find them again.

- Ask for alternative answers and agree on which solutions work and which do not. Encourage children to use real coins to find solutions.

- Rub out the coins and totals.

- Write the totals 7p and 6p for the rows and 3p and 10p for the columns.

- *Which coins shall I use to make these totals?*

- *Where should I put them? How do you know?*

## Independent, paired or group work

- Ask the children to complete resource page A. Give them a selection of coins to help.

- Tell the children that they are allowed to use more than one of any coin value.

- Early finishers could set similar coin puzzles for a partner.

## Plenary

- Invite the children to show their work.

- *Who found an easy way to solve these puzzles?*

- Show them the following method for solving the problems:

  - Always start by finding the sets of two coins.

  - If the sets of three coins do not add up correctly, change the order of one of the sets of two coins.

  - Keep changing the order of the sets of two coins until you get the correct answer for the three coins.

Name: _____

# Coin puzzle

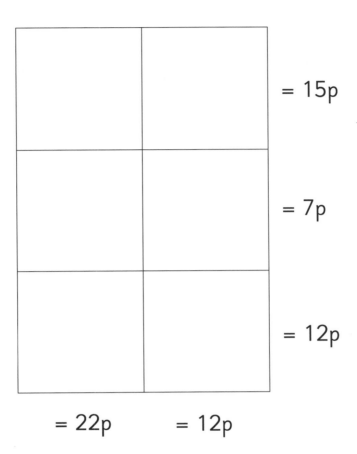

= 15p

= 7p

= 12p

= 22p        = 12p

= 32p

= 27p

= 25p        = 4p        = 30p

# Two-coin puzzles

Oral/mental starter p 182

**Advance Organiser**

We are going to find different ways to solve more complex coin puzzles

**You will need:** 1p, 2p, 5p, 10p and 20p coins, resource page B

## Whole-class work

- Draw the following coin diagram on the board.

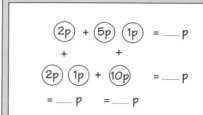

- *Who can tell me about this puzzle? Can anyone see what we have to do?*

- Encourage the children to look at the equals signs and deduce that they should add the coins in each row and column.

- *Who can add these coins? How did you do that?*

- *Does anyone know another way of adding these coins?*

- *Does anyone get a different total?*

- Rub out the coins' values, leaving the totals.

- Ask the children to suggest which coins make those totals, encouraging them to look for alternative answers.

- Rub out the coins and totals and replace them with the totals 6p and 30p for the rows and 12p and 24p for the columns.

- *Which coins should I use to make these totals?*

- *How can I find out?*

- Demonstrate a methodical strategy if one is not suggested.

- *Start by finding three coins that make 6p.*

- *If this is a 2p coin, what other two coins do we add to make 12p?*

## Independent, paired or group work

- Ask the children to complete resource page B. Give them real coins to help.

## Plenary

- Invite the children to show their work.

- Show the following method for solving the problems:

  - Start by finding totals made from two coins.

  - Next, find totals made from three coins.

  - Check that the totals made from two sets of coins are correct.

  - Check that the totals made from three sets of coins are correct.

  - Change the order of the two sets of coins, if necessary.

**PUPIL PAGE**

Name: _____

# Two-coin puzzles

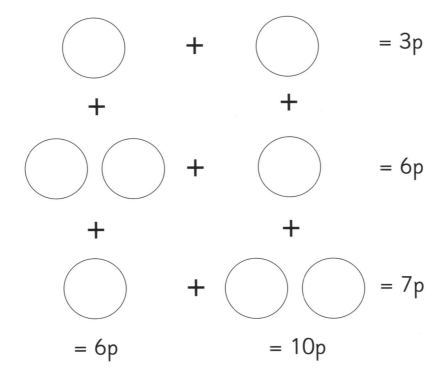

$$\bigcirc + \bigcirc = 3p$$
$$+ \qquad +$$
$$\bigcirc\bigcirc + \bigcirc = 6p$$
$$+ \qquad +$$
$$\bigcirc \quad + \quad \bigcirc\bigcirc = 7p$$
$$= 6p \qquad = 10p$$

$$\bigcirc + \bigcirc + \bigcirc = 20p$$
$$+ \qquad + \qquad +$$
$$\bigcirc\bigcirc + \bigcirc\bigcirc + \bigcirc = 19p$$
$$= 13p \qquad = 16p \qquad = 10p$$

*Classworks* © Classworks Numeracy author team, Nelson Thornes Ltd, 2003

# Nine coins

**Oral/mental starter
p 182**

**Advance Organiser**

We are going to find different ways to solve puzzles with nine coins

**You will need:** 1p, 2p, 5p, 10p and 20p coins, resource page C

## Whole-class work

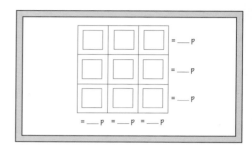

- Draw the following diagram on the board.

- *Who can tell me about this puzzle? Who thinks they know what we have to do?*

- Write 2p or 5p on the squares in each grid square.

- Ask the children to help work out the six totals.

- Rub out the coins and totals and write the totals 6p, 15p and 3p for the rows, and 8p, 8p and 8p for the columns.

- *What do you notice about this puzzle?*

- Point out that the coins in the three columns make a total of 8p in each column.

- *Which total shall we start with?*

- Children may wish to start by identifying the bottom row as being three 1p coins.

- *What three coins make 6p? Which three coins make 15p?*

- Write the values of the coins on the diagram and check to see that the coins add up to make each total.

## Independent, paired or group work

- Ask the children to complete resource page C.

- Give them real coins as support.

## Plenary

- Invite the children to share their work.

- Write the totals 15p, 11p and 11p for the rows and 11p, 11p and 15p for the columns.

- *This is one way to solve the problem.*

- *Start by finding 3 coins that make 15p.*

- Write on the board: $5p + 5p + 5p = 15p$.

- Write 5p in each of the squares in the top row and right-hand column.

- *We need to add two coins to the 5p to make 11p.*

- Show how changing the position of these last four coins can alter the totals.

Name: _____

# Nine coins

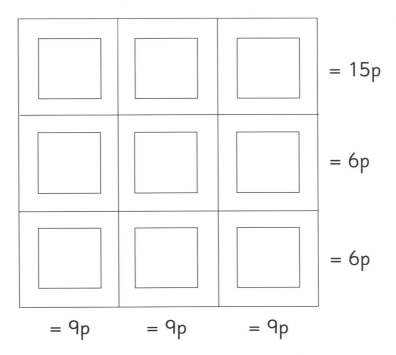

= 15p

= 6p

= 6p

= 9p     = 9p     = 9p

= 15p

= 14p

= 13p

= 25p     = 8p     = 9p

# Solving Problems (6)

**Outcome**

*Children will be able to use cubes to find double and half of a number less than 10*

| **Medium-term plan objectives** | • Choose and use the appropriate number operations and mental strategies to solve simple money or 'real life' problems using counting, addition or subtraction, halving or doubling. |
|---|---|

| **Overview** | • Find doubles of small numbers. |
|---|---|
| | • Use knowledge of doubles to find halves of small numbers. |
| | • Find missing numbers using knowledge of halves and doubles. |

## How you could plan this unit

| | Stage 1 | Stage 2 | Stage 3 | Stage 4 | Stage 5 |
|---|---|---|---|---|---|
| **Content and vocabulary** | Doubles<br><br>*twice, double* | Finding halves of towers<br><br>*halve, half* | Halves and doubles<br><br>*twice, double, halve, half, smallest, largest, middle* | | |
| **Notes** | | This stage is similar to Stage 1, but this time challenging children to make towers half as high. They can have a tower to break into two halves to begin with, then move on to giving an answer first and checking using cubes | Resource pages A and B | | |

# *Doubles*

Oral/mental starter
p 182

**Adance Organiser**

We are going to make a tower twice as high

**You will need:** small pieces of paper, linking cubes

## Whole-class work

- Show the children a tower made from four linking cubes.
- Count the cubes with the children.
- Write '4' on a label next to the tower.
- *I'm going to make another tower that is twice as high.*
- *Who can help me to build the tower?*
- Build two more 4-towers and put them together to make an 8-tower.
- Count the cubes with the children and write '8' on a label.
- Point to each tower as you say: *There are twice as many cubes in this tower as in this tower.*
- *Twice 4 is 8.*
- Split the 8-tower back into two 4-towers.
- *Two 4-towers make one 8-tower.*
- Repeat, starting with a tower of six cubes.

## Independent, paired or group work

- Ask the children to build towers of two to six cubes and then make them twice as high.
- They could record their work by drawing the towers and their 'doubles' and writing the number of cubes in each.

## Plenary

- Display a line of 'doubles' towers with labels showing the number of cubes in each.
- For example: 1 cube, 2 cubes, 4 cubes and 8 cubes.
- Point to the towers as you say: *This tower is twice as high as this tower.*
- Introduce the term 'double' to mean 'twice'.
- *Twice 4 is 8. Double 4 is 8.*
- Demonstrate that the 8-tower can be split into two equal towers of four.
- *One tower of 8 makes two towers of 4. Two towers of 4 make one tower of 8.*
- Write on the board: *4 + 4 = 8* and *Twice 4 makes 8.*

# Halves and doubles

**Advance Organiser**

We are going to make sets of towers twice as high and half as high

**Oral/mental starter p 182**

**You will need:** linking cubes, resource page A (enlarged), resource page B (one per child)

## Whole-class work

- Show the children an enlarged copy of resource page A.
- *What can you tell me about these towers?*
- *The largest tower is made from twice as many cubes as the middle tower.*
- *The middle tower is made from twice as many cubes as the smallest tower.*
- *The smallest tower is made from half as many cubes as the middle tower.*
- *The middle tower is made from half as many cubes as the largest tower.*
- Show a tower made from four cubes.
- *This is the largest tower. How many cubes in the middle tower?*
- Write '4' on the largest tower in the diagram.
- *The middle tower is half as high as this tower.*
- Ask the children to tell you how many cubes are in the middle tower.
- *How do you know?*
- *How many cubes are in the smallest tower?*
- Write '8' on the largest tower and repeat.
- Now begin with the smallest tower.
- *I have three cubes in my smallest tower.*
- *The middle tower is twice as high. How many cubes in the middle tower?*
- *The largest tower is twice as high again. How many cubes in the largest tower?*

## Independent, paired or group work

- Ask the children to complete resource page B. They have to make each tower, then write the number of cubes each time.
- Early finishers might try doubling the number of bricks in the largest towers.

## Plenary

- Invite the children to show their sets of towers.
- Show one of the children's towers and ask the class to tell you the number of cubes in the other towers.
- *This is the smallest tower.*
- *It's made with five cubes.*
- *How many cubes are in the tower that is twice as high as this?*

# Halves and doubles

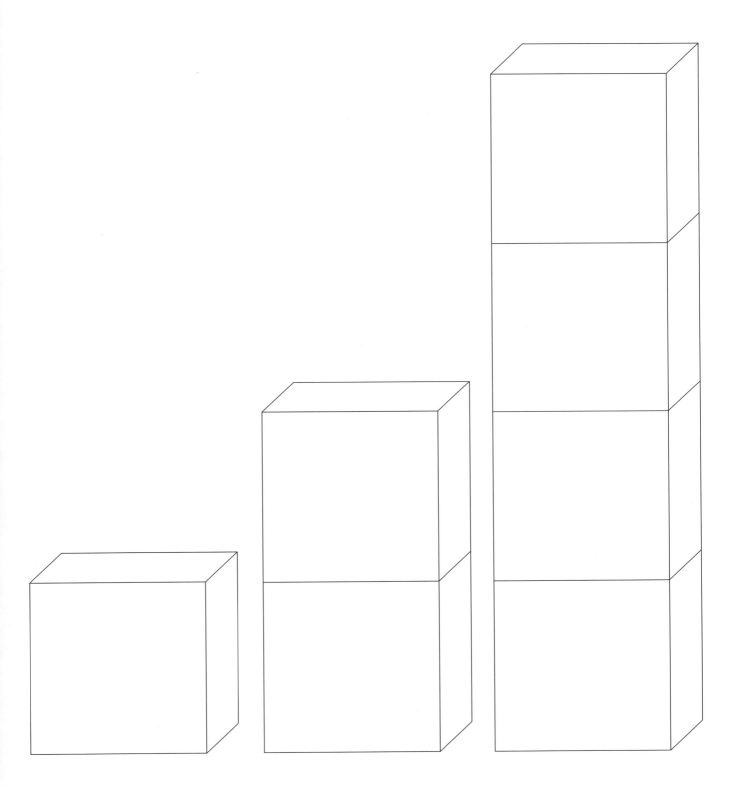

Name: _____

# Halves and doubles

Make a tower 4 cubes high.

Make a tower half as high. How many cubes in this tower? ☐

Make a tower half as high again. How many cubes in this tower? ☐

Make a tower 2 cubes high.

Make a tower twice as high. How many cubes in this tower? ☐

Make a tower twice as high again. How many cubes in this tower? ☐

Make a tower 6 cubes high.

Make a tower half as high. How many cubes in this tower? ☐

Make a tower twice as high as the tower with 6 cubes.

How many cubes in this tower? ☐

# Measures (1)

### Outcome

*Children can say which length is the longest/shortest*

**Medium-term plan objectives**

- Understand and use the vocabulary related to length and time.
- Compare two, then more, lengths using direct comparison.
- Measure lengths using uniform non-standard units or standard units; for example, metre sticks.
- Order familiar events.

**Overview**

- Compare lengths of pairs of objects using *longer* and *shorter.*
- Compare lengths of more than two objects using *longest* and *shortest.*
- Introduce and use the vocabulary *longer than* and *shorter than.*

## How you could plan this unit

| | Stage 1 | Stage 2 | Stage 3 | Stage 4 | Stage 5 |
|---|---|---|---|---|---|
| **Content and vocabulary** | Comparing the lengths of two objects<br><br>*longer, shorter* | Comparing the lengths of more than two objects<br><br>*longest, shortest* | Using uniform non-standard units<br><br>*longer than, shorter than* | Vocabulary of time, ordering familiar events in time | |
| **Notes** | Resource pages A and B | Resource page C | | | |

117

# Comparing the lengths of two objects

**Advance Organiser**

We are going to find out which pencil is longer

Oral/mental starter
p 183

**You will need:** two pencils of clearly different lengths, two pencils of similar but different lengths, Blu-Tack, whiteboard or flipchart, resource page A, resource page B

## Whole-class work

- Hold up two pencils of clearly different lengths in separate hands. Hold and move them in a variety of ways and positions.

- *Which is **longer**? Show me how you decided. Which is **shorter**?*

- Look at resource page A for a quick refresher of how children progress in recognising length in comparison.

- Repeat with two pencils of similar but different lengths.

- *Can we tell which of these is longer? How could we find out?*

- Blu-Tack them next to each other on the whiteboard with a vertical reference line.

- *Which is longer? Which is shorter? Show me how you decided this time.*

- Summarise the conclusion when it is reached, and write it on the board: *The red pencil is longer than the blue pencil. The blue pencil is shorter than the red pencil.*

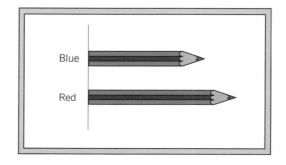

- Repeat with other pairs of pencils.

## Independent, paired or group work

- Ask the children to complete resource page B.

- The alignments get more difficult towards the bottom of the page.

- Common difficulties are illustrated on resource page A.

- Some children will compare visually, some will use their fingers, a stick of cubes or a line of counters.

## Plenary

- Use resource sheet A to revise more challenging alignments of two pencils.

- Ask children to explain how they can find out which pencil is longer.

- *How do you know?*

( EXAMPLE )

# Progression of comparing the lengths of two objects

**Stage A** – both objects are horizontal and parallel

Aligned left

Aligned right

One contained within the other

Overlapping

**Stage B** – both objects are vertical and parallel

**Stage C** – one object is horizontal, one is vertical (at right angles)

**Stage D** – the objects are at angles to one another

Overlapping

Aligned on horizontal parallels

Name: _____

# Ring the right word each time

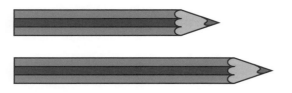   This pencil is  shorter  longer

This pencil is  shorter  longer

   This pencil is  shorter  longer

This pencil is  shorter  longer

   This pencil is  shorter  longer

This pencil is  shorter  longer

This pencil is
shorter  longer

This pencil is
shorter  longer

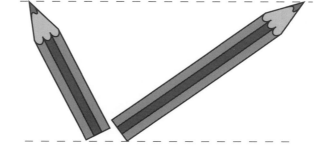

This pencil is
shorter  longer

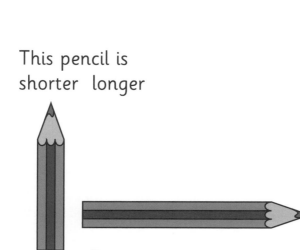

This pencil is  shorter  longer

# *Comparing the lengths of more than two objects*

**Advance Organiser**

We are going to find out which pencil is the longest

**You will need:** Blu-Tack, whiteboard or flipchart, four different coloured pencils of varying lengths, resource page C or drawing of three coloured straws – longest yellow, shortest red and intermediate green

**Oral/mental starter p 183**

## Whole-class work

- Stick a red pencil to a whiteboard or flipchart using Blu-Tack and align the end to a vertical reference line.

- Add a second, longer green pencil, also aligned.

- *Which pencil is longer? How did you decide that?*

- Agree that: *The green pencil is longer than the red pencil. The red pencil is shorter than the green pencil.*

- Add a third, longer yellow pencil.

- *Is the yellow pencil longer or shorter than the green pencil?*

- Agree that: *The yellow pencil is even longer than the green pencil.*

- *Which is the **longest** pencil?*

- Test the children's answer by pointing in turn to the other two pencils and asking: *Which is longer?*

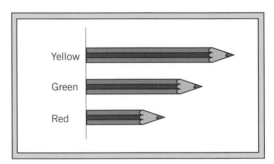

- Confirm the conclusion: *Yes, the yellow pencil is the **longest** because it is **longer** than the green pencil and **longer** than the red pencil.*

- Repeat the above routine and ask which is the **shortest**.

- Add a fourth, even longer blue pencil and ask: *Is the yellow pencil still the longest?*

## Independent, paired or group work

- Ask the children to complete resource page C.

- Some children will compare the objects visually, some will use their fingers, a stick of cubes or a line of counters.

- The alignments of the objects become progressively more complex as the children work down the page. See resource page A for a summary of the progression of difficulty in comparing lengths.

## Plenary

- Look together at selected children's completed activity sheets.

- Ask questions of the class based on the sheets.

- *Is the red pen **shorter** than the others? How did you decide?*

Name: _____

# Longest and shortest

Colour **red** the shortest in each group.
Colour **yellow** the longest in each group.

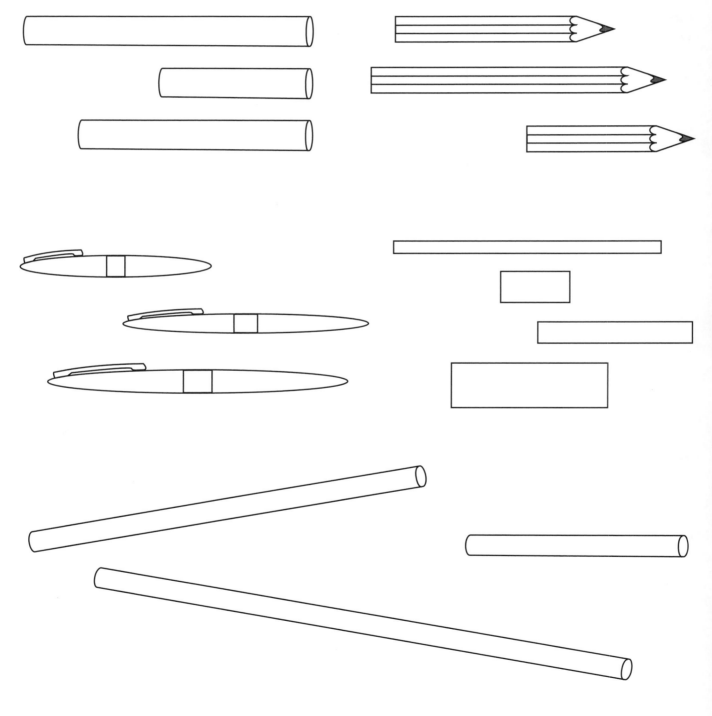

# Using uniform non-standard units

**Advance Organiser**

We are going to measure using our hand spans

Oral/mental starter
p 183

**You will need:** collection of items from the classroom (pens, crayons, brushes, tins, trays), Venn diagram rings labelled *longer than my hand span* and *shorter than my hand span* on the board

## Whole-class work

- Choose a child and announce that we are going to measure things using their hand span. Stretch out your hand to show the child how to use their span.

- One at a time, compare various items like pens or crayons to the child's hand span and place it in the correct set.

- Ask another child with a hand of similar size to check the items in each set one at a time.

- Now decide to check the items yourself with your own hand and make a pretend fuss when you find items that are in the 'wrong' set. *Why are these in the wrong set?*

- Compare your span to that of the first child. Compare the child's span with other children's spans, using *longer* and *shorter*.

- Draw out from the class that to be able to compare lots of measures accurately we should use the same hand span each time.

- Draw around one child's hand and also draw a line from the tip of their little finger to the tip of their thumb to show the span. Cut out the hand and demonstrate by using it as a measure. Retitle the Venn sets *longer than one hand span*, and *shorter than one hand span*.

- Discuss what could be placed in each Venn ring.

## Independent, paired or group work

- Ask the children to find and write three things to go in each set. They use the same hand-span each time.

## Plenary

- Look together at selected children's completed work.

- Ask them to fetch the items they measured and sort them into sets in the Venn rings.

- Ask the class if they recorded the same items in the same sets. Discuss any differences.

- Ask all the children to bring the hand span that they used. Compare them to show that they have all used the same-sized measure. Discuss how many hand-spans long each object is. Write a list of these on the board.

# Measures (2)

**Outcome**

*Children can estimate length and order events in time*

| **Medium-term plan objectives** | |
|---|---|
| | • Suggest suitable non-standard units and measuring equipment to estimate, then measure a length and record estimates and measurements as 'X and a bit'. |
| | • Solve simple problems involving length or time. |
| | • Know days of the week. |
| | • Read time to the hour on analogue clocks. |

| **Overview** | |
|---|---|
| | • Establish the idea of estimating a length (guessing what the result will be) before measuring. |
| | • Look at the order of days in terms of yesterday, today, tomorrow and by name. |
| | • Sequence times shown on clock faces linked to events. |

## How you could plan this unit

| | Stage 1 | Stage 2 | Stage 3 | Stage 4 | Stage 5 |
|---|---|---|---|---|---|
| **Content and vocabulary** | Estimating and measuring height<br><br>*length, height, long, short, tall, high, low, metre, metre sticks* | Solving problems involving length<br><br>*length, height, long, short, tall, high, low, metre, metre sticks* | Ordering days of the week<br><br>*Monday, Tuesday ...,  day, week, before, after, next, last* | Reading time on a clock<br><br>*hour, o'clock, clock, watch, hands, bedtime, dinnertime, playtime* | |
| **Notes** | | Ask children first to estimate, then to discuss how to measure, the length of the classroom in metre-sticks. | Resource page A | Resource page B | |

124

# *Estimating and measuring height*

**Advance Organiser**

We are going to make a good guess of our own height and check our good guess

**Oral/mental starter p 183**

**You will need:** a metre stick per pair, two long skipping ropes, *longer* and *shorter* labels

## Whole-class work

- Show the children a metre stick. Explain what it is.

- *Who can tell me someone who is taller than this metre stick?*

- Compare the child to the metre stick.

- *How can you tell that Harry is taller than the metre stick?*

- Compare Harry to the stick to check and agree the decision with the class.

- Make two groups with the skipping ropes and labels and ask Harry to stand in the appropriate group.

- Repeat with at least six more children.

- Choose children to check with the metre stick if the class have made the correct decision each time.

- Show the class the metre stick again.

> **Harry is taller than the metre stick**

## Independent, paired or group work

- Give each group of 4 children a metre stick and ask them to estimate, then measure who is taller or shorter than the metre stick. They record both estimates and measures.

- They can draw a smiley or sad face according to how close they think their estimates were.

## Plenary

- Talk through some estimates for each group. Measure and check some results with the class.

- Discuss any differences and how they might have occurred – whether some children measured more carefully and so on. Demonstrate measuring carefully against the wall.

# Ordering days of the week

Oral/mental starter
p 183

**Advance Organiser**

We are going to order the days of the week and talk about what we do on each day

**You will need:** days of the week flashcards, resource page A

## Whole-class work

- Shuffle the flashcards, let a child choose one and place it in a gap on a diagram like the one below. Read it.

- *Who can tell me which day comes next?*

- Choose from remaining days and place it in the next gap.

- *Who thinks this is right?*

- Repeat for another day and again agree the correct place with the child.

- Put the remaining five flashcards on the circle.

- Remove cards, shuffle, choose and repeat starting with a different day and with a different gap.

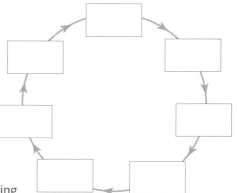

- Read through the days in sequence again. Ask some quick questions.

- *Which day comes after …?*

- *Which day comes before …?*

- Draw out from the children that Saturday and Sunday are different in some ways from the rest of the week.

- *Which days are written in a different colour?*

- *What is different about these two days?*

- *Which days do you come to school?*

- Discuss what children might do on Saturday and Sunday.

## Independent, paired or group work

- Ask the children to complete resource page A.

- They should then write 'at home' or 'at school' for each day.

## Plenary

- Complete a large version of resource page A with the class.

- *Who comes to school on Sunday, Monday, Tuesday, etc.?*

- Shuffle flash cards and ask: *What day comes before/after …?*

# Days of the week

Name: _____

Monday

Write in the missing days and join them up.

# Reading time on a clock

**Advance Organiser**

We are going to read the time and talk about when we do things

**You will need:** geared analogue clock face, resource page B (one enlarged and one per child)

**Whole-class work**

- Use a large analogue clock face (with auto-winding hour hand).

- Lead the class through chanting the hours and read out the times in sequence.

- Ask the class to go through hours for a full day saying in turn what they might be doing.

- Write some ideas on the board.

- Look at a large version of resource page B and talk through the events.

- *When do you get up in the morning?*

- *Does anyone get up at a different time?*

> 8 o'clock in the morning, waking up and climbing out of bed
>
> 9 o'clock at night **should be** fast asleep
>
> 10 o'clock at night **still** asleep

**Independent, paired or group work**

- Ask the children to complete resource page B by drawing the hour hand on and writing in the missing numerals.

**Plenary**

- Look again at an enlarged version of resource page B.

- Ask selected children which times they put in for which events.

- Fill the sheet in for yourself by asking the class to help you – ask children to suggest what time you go to bed, when they think you leave school, and so on.

- Ask the class to think about various actions in the day and how long they spend on them.

- *How long do you spend in bed each day?*

- *How long do you think it is between getting up and having dinner?*

- *How did you decide that?*

- Count on together from the relevant hours with the clock face to check the children's answers.

Name: _____

**1** I get up in the morning at ............. o'clock

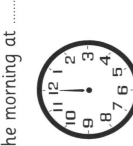

**2** School starts at ............. o'clock

**3** I have my lunch at ............. o'clock

**4** I have my tea at ............. o'clock

**5** I go to bed at ............. o'clock

**6** I am fast asleep at ............. o'clock

*Classworks* © Classworks Numeracy author team, Nelson Thornes Ltd, 2003

# Measures (3)

**Outcome**

*Children can say which object is heavier*

| | |
|---|---|
| **Medium-term plan objectives** | • Understand and use the vocabulary related to mass. |
| | • Compare two, then more, masses using direct comparison. |
| | • Measure mass using uniform non-standard units. |
| **Overview** | • Practise using the vocabulary *heavy* and *light*, *heavier than* and *lighter than*. |
| | • Use a balance to compare masses and use appropriate comparative language. |
| | • Measure mass of objects using a balance and uniform but non-standard units. |

## How you could plan this unit

| | Stage 1 | Stage 2 | Stage 3 | Stage 4 | Stage 5 |
|---|---|---|---|---|---|
| **Content and vocabulary** | Comparing two masses<br><br>*compare, nearly, roughly, close to, about the same as, just over, just under, weighs, weigh, balances, heavy/light, heavier than/ lighter than, scales, weight, balance* | Comparing more than two masses<br><br>*heaviest, lightest* | Measuring mass<br><br>*measure, guess, estimate, too many, too few* | | |
| **Notes** | Resource page A | Follow a similar structure to stage 1, using three items, confirming that the *heaviest* item is *heavier than* each of the other items. | Resource page B | | |

# Comparing two masses

**Advance Organiser**

We are going to find out which object is heavier

Oral/mental starter
p 183

**You will need:** balances (both suspended and see-saw types), a collection of classroom objects (cubes, blocks, toys, stationery, etc.), resource page A, Venn rings, labels *heavy*, *light*, *is heavier than*, *is lighter than*

## Whole-class work

- Use the labels as flash cards to practise quickly recognising the words and phrases *heavy*, *light*, *is heavier than* and *is lighter than*.

- Pick up a succession of objects and show them to the children.

- *Do you think the scissors are heavy or light?*

- Start to sort the objects into two Venn rings labelled *heavy* and *light*. After a few objects have been sorted into each hoop, or if a child raises a question, pause.

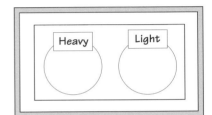

- *How can we decide if the scissors are heavier than the cube?*

- Ask the children to hold the objects and compare them.

- Introduce the balances.

- *I am going to put the scissors in this pan and the cube in this pan.*

- *Do you think that the scissors are heavier than the cube? What will happen to the balances? Why do you think that?*

- Test the two objects using both types of balance.

- With the children, decide which is heavier, which is lighter.

- *Why does this object go down? Why does this object go up?*

- *The scissors are heavier than the cube.*

- Look at the first section of an enlarged version of resource page A.

- *Should the wooden block go on the higher side if the pencil is on the lower side? Why did you decide that?*

- Draw the objects on the resource page and complete the sentence.

## Independent, paired or group work

- Ask the children to work in pairs and to complete resource page A using pairs of objects such as: a pencil and a roll of sellotape, a centimetre cube and a wooden block.

## Plenary

- Look at a few children's recordings on their copies of resource page A.

- Let everyone 'guess' which is the heavier or lighter of two objects. One child then feels the objects to check. They can use the balance if necessary.

- Ask three children to fetch a pair of objects they used.

- Check their decisions using the balance and record on the enlarged version of resource page A.

Name: _____

# Which is heavier? Which is lighter?

The ............................... is **heavier than** the ...............................

The ............................... is **lighter than** the ...............................

The ............................... is **heavier than** the ...............................

The ............................... is **lighter than** the ...............................

# *Measuring mass*

**Advance organiser**

We are going to find out how many cubes we need to balance a wooden block

**Oral/mental starter p 183**

**You will need:** balances, a collection of classroom objects (blocks, books, toys, etc.), a large set of linking cubes (grouped in 5s or 10s), resource page B

---

**Whole-class work**

- Show the children a wooden block and some linking cubes.
- *How many cubes do you think I need to balance this block?*
- Ask the children at the front of the class to hold the block and the cubes.
- Demonstrate balancing the block with cubes, counting out the cubes one by one with the class. Say, and write on the board, different ways of recording your result.
- *I needed fourteen cubes to balance the wooden block.*
- *The wooden block weighs the same as fourteen cubes.*
- *The wooden block has the same mass as fourteen cubes.*
- Record the result on an enlarged version of resource page B.
- Before measuring a second object, announce that you know a way to make the counting easier.
- Line up a 10-stick and a 5-stick of joined cubes. Count how many in each stick with the children.
- Now balance the second object adding sticks of cubes, counting in fives or tens.
- When the cubes weigh more than the object, say: *What has happened? Can anyone explain why?*
- Confirm that now: *There is a greater mass in this pan. The cubes weigh more than the block.*
- *What should I do now to make the cubes balance?*
- Remove a stick and add single cubes until the pans balance.
- Record the result on resource page B.

---

**Independent, paired or group work**

- Ask the children to work in pairs with some objects, some identical cubes and balances.
- They can record their results on resource page B.

---

**Plenary**

- *Which do you think is the heaviest of all the objects?*
- Ask a child to choose the object that they think is the heaviest.
- Check this on the balance.
- Stress again that: *The heavier side goes down, and the lighter side goes up.*
- Repeat for a few other objects until you have established the *heaviest*.
- Repeat for the *lightest* object.

Name: _____

# How many cubes?

I needed ................. cubes to balance this ................................

I needed ................. cubes to balance this ................................

I needed ................. cubes to balance this ................................

# Measures (4)

**Outcome**

*Children can measure and record mass*

| | |
|---|---|
| **Medium-term plan objectives** | • Suggest suitable (non) standard units and measuring equipment to estimate, then measure, mass, recording estimates and measurement as *'about as heavy as 20 cubes'*. |
| | • Know seasons of the year. |
| **Overview** | • Selecting and using non-standard but uniform units to measure mass. |
| | • Making estimates of mass using non-standard but uniform units. |

## How you could plan this unit

| | Stage 1 | Stage 2 | Stage 3 | Stage 4 | Stage 5 |
|---|---|---|---|---|---|
| **Content and vocabulary** | Using uniform non-standard units<br><br>*measure, too many, too few, nearly, roughly, close to, about the same as, just over, just under, weigh, weighs, balances, heavy, light, heavier, lighter, heaviest, lightest, weight, balance, scales* | Estimating and measuring mass<br><br>*guess, estimate* | Solving problems involving mass | Know seasons of the year | |
| **Notes** | | Resource page A | Resource page B | Rehearse the cyclical order of the season, starting at different points. Ask children what season they think they were born in, then check by asking which month and discussing with the class. | |

# *Using uniform non-standard units*

**Advance Organiser**

We are going to find out how many pieces of pasta balance the toy and how many counters balance the toy

**Oral/mental starter p 183**

**You will need:** objects to weigh (such as assortments of beads, pasta, counters, beans, tiddlywinks, straws, cubes, books (for example, reading scheme books, and so on), cards with the names of each unit and a sample unit stuck on each one

## Whole-class work

- Balance an object that you know is lighter than a cube, for example, a small toy, a plastic cotton reel, or similar, with a single cube.

- *Can anyone tell me how I can measure the toy's mass?*

- *What could we use to try to balance the toy?*

- Display the selection of cards showing the name of each unit (balancing object) and an example of that unit. Take suggestions and try balancing the toy using those units.

BEAD

- *How many beads weigh the same as the toy? How many tiddlywinks weigh the same as the toy?*

- Record the results of balancing the toy with different units (balancing objects).

- *Which unit did we need more of to balance the toy? Can anyone tell me why that is?*

- Choose another toy to weigh and discuss which unit (balancing object) might be best (a lighter or heavier unit (balancing object) depending on the mass of the toy).

- Balance it and record the results with the children.

## Independent, paired or group work

- Ask the children to work in pairs to choose one toy to balance with different units, recording their work.

- Repeat for a second toy.

- As an extension, ask the children to balance three different toys and to choose which non-standard units to use.

## Plenary

- Choose a very light toy.

- Discuss which units (balancing objects) could be used to balance the toy.

- Discuss who used what as balancing objects in their work.

- *Which of the non-standard units was best for heavier and lighter objects?*

- *Which non-standard units were the easiest to use? Which were the best to use for each object? Why do you think that is?*

# Estimating and measuring mass

**Advance Organiser**

We are going to make an estimate (a good guess) and check

Oral/mental starter
p 183

**You will need:** rulers, books, linking cubes, balances, resource page A (one enlarged and one per pair)

## Whole-class work

- Balance a reading book using identical cubes and record how many on the board.

- Add an identical reading book to the same pan.

- *Can you make a good guess, an* **estimate**, *of how many cubes will be needed to balance two books? Why do you think that?*

- Record different estimates. Balance the two and see if some of the estimates were close.

- Select another storybook and ask for estimates of how many cubes will balance it.

- Choose one estimate with the class and record it on an enlarged version of resource page A.

- Balance the storybook and record the result. Discuss: *How close were we?*

- Choose a face on resource page A according to how close the chosen estimate was, ranging from 😦 (nowhere near), 😐 to 😊 (very close or exactly right).

## Independent, paired or group work

- Ask the children to work in pairs (or small groups) and complete resource page A.

- They should first agree on an estimate, then balance, and finally decide how close their guess was to the result.

- Guide children towards using their experience.

- *If you needed ten cubes to balance the pencil and you think that the book is heavier than the pencil, how many cubes do you think you will need to balance the book?*

## Plenary

- List some of the children's estimates for each of the three items in resource page A in turn, together with the exact number of cubes that each item balanced.

- *Which object was the easiest to estimate? Why?*

( **PUPIL PAGE** )

Name: _____

# A good guess

I estimate the book is about as heavy as ................... cubes.

It needs ................ cubes to balance it.

My estimate was ☹ , 😐 , 🙂

I estimate the ruler is about as heavy as ................ cubes.

It needs ................ cubes to balance it.

My estimate was ☹ , 😐 , 🙂

I estimate the scissors are about as heavy as ................ cubes.

It needs ................ cubes to balance it.

My estimate was ☹ , 😐 , 🙂

# *Solving problems involving mass*

**Advance Organiser**

We are going to decide how many cubes we need to add to the pencil to make it balance the scissors

**Oral/mental starter p 183**

**You will need:** children's scissors, pencils, balances, cubes, resource page B (one enlarged and one per pair)

## Whole-class work

- Balance a pencil using cubes.
- Count together how many cubes balance the pencil.
- Replace the pencil with a pair of children's scissors.
- *How many more cubes do you think we need to balance the scissors?*
- Check.
- Put the pencil in one pan and the scissors in the other.
- *How many cubes will we need to add to the pencil to make it balance the scissors?*
- Check to see if the pencil and the number of cubes will balance the scissors.
- Use an enlarged copy of resource page B to record, drawing what happened in the box. Draw squares to represent the number of cubes in the empty pan.
- *Were we right?*
- Complete the face (smiley, indifferent or sad) to show how well you did.
- Repeat this procedure using two pencils instead of one and one pair of scissors.
- *Will more or fewer cubes be needed to balance? Why did you decide that?*

## Independent, paired or group work

- Ask the children to work in pairs (or small groups) and complete resource page B.
- Remind them that they may get different results because the pencils (and perhaps scissors) vary in size.
- As an extension, some children could try again using two pencils to balance against the scissors.

## Plenary

- Demonstrate measuring a new object using cubes. Record the result.
- Compare the new object with one of the pairs of scissors the children measured.
- *The scissors weighed the same as 23 cubes. This bag of marbles weighs the same as 34 cubes. Who can help me make a good guess of how many cubes I should add to the scissors to balance the marbles?*
- Ask different children to help you solve the problem.
- *How did we decide?*
- Write up the children's ideas on the board and discuss how they can use what they know already to solve different problems.

**PUPIL PAGE**

Name: _____

# Balancing cubes

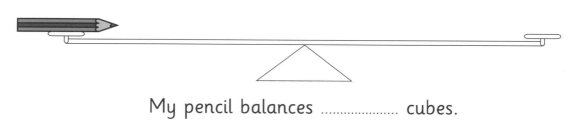

My pencil balances .................... cubes.

The scissors balance .................... cubes.

The scissors need .................... more cubes than my pencil.

I add cubes to the pencil to balance the scissors.
How many cubes do I need?
I think:

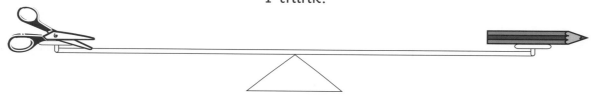

I checked:

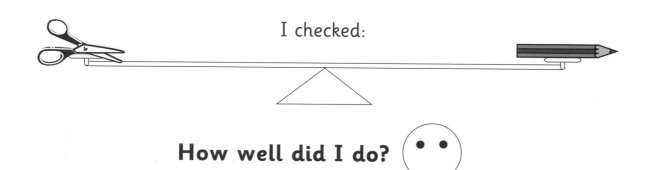

**How well did I do?**

# Measures (5)

**Outcome**

*Children can compare two capacities and measure capacity*

| Medium-term plan objectives | |
|---|---|
| | • Understand and use the vocabulary related to capacity. |
| | • Compare two, then more, capacities using direct comparisons. |
| | • Measure capacity using uniform non-standard units or standard units (litre). |

**Overview**

- Introduce appropriate vocabulary.
- Direct comparison of capacities.
- Introduce uniform non-standard units.

## How you could plan this unit

| | Stage 1 | Stage 2 | Stage 3 | Stage 4 | Stage 5 |
|---|---|---|---|---|---|
| **Content and vocabulary** | Comparing capacity<br><br>compare, nearly, just over, just under, close to, about the same as, too much, too little, roughly, full, holds, container, empty, too much | Comparing more than two capacities<br><br>most, least | Measuring capacity<br><br>measure, guess, estimate | Introducing standard units (the litre) | |
| **Notes** | | Use a similar structure to stage 1 to discuss comparing more than two capacities | | Relate the litre unit to a litre-capacity squash bottle, building on the concept of a standard unit from Stage 3 | |

# *Comparing capacity*

Oral/mental starter
p 183

**Advance Organiser**

We are going to find out which container holds more water

**You will need:** plastic cup, jug, wide-necked 1 litre bottle, funnel, tray, towel

## Whole-class work

- Place a plastic cup on a tray next to a wide-necked 1 litre pop bottle.

- *Which do you think holds more?*

- Use a jug to fill the cup up to the top. Use the words *full* and *holds* throughout.

- Ask: *Is the cup full?*

- Use a funnel to pour the water from the cup into the bottle.

- *Is the bottle full?*

- Agree that the bottle will hold more liquid than this.

- Fill the bottle up to the top.

- *Is there enough water in the bottle to fill the cup? How do you know?*

- Pour the water from the bottle into the cup until the cup is full.

- *Is the cup full? Is the bottle full? Which holds more, the cup or the bottle? How do you know?*

- Record your results on the board. Now compare the bottle's capacity with that of the jug in a similar way.

- Establish which of the three containers holds the most and which the least.

- *How did you decide that?*

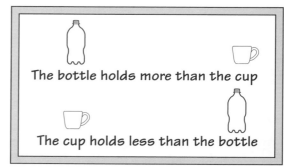

The bottle holds more than the cup

The cup holds less than the bottle

## Independent, paired or group work

- Practise vocabulary by comparing the three containers and asking the children to call out the correct word in sentences such as:

- *The bottle holds ...... than the cup. The cup holds ...... than the jug. The bottle holds ...... than the jug but ...... than the cup.*

## Plenary

- Place the three containers on the table and ask the children to put them in order, starting with the one which holds the most.

- Repeat, starting with the one which holds the least.

# *Measuring capacity*

**Advance Organiser**

We are going to find out how many cups of water fill each bottle

Oral/mental starter
p 183

**You will need:** two different-sized plastic bottles with labels (lemonade bottle, squash bottle), beaker and cup (different sizes), jug, tray, bucket or bowl for waste water, funnel and towel

## Whole-class work

- *I want you to help me count how many beakers of water will fill the lemonade bottle.*

- Fill the lemonade bottle to the top using the beaker as a measure.

- Record how many beakers were needed on the board.

- *Now I want you to make good guesses (estimates) of how many times I can fill this cup using the water in the lemonade bottle.*

- Record the estimates on the board.

- Hold the cup over the bucket and count together each time the cup is filled from the lemonade bottle.

- When this is done, confirm and record the result.

- Use language such as *about*, *nearly*, *just over* and so on, as appropriate.

- *Why did we need more cups of water to fill the lemonade bottle?*

> We needed 8 beakers
> of water to fill the
> lemonade bottle

> We needed just over
> 12 cups of water to
> fill the lemonade bottle

## Independent, paired or group work

- Ask the children to help you repeat the activity using the squash bottle, pausing after measuring with the beaker.

- *We needed 7 beakers of water to fill the squash bottle. Do you think we will need the same number, more, or fewer cups to fill the squash bottle? Why do you think that?*

- Ask the children to discuss, in pairs, their estimates of how many cups of water will fill the squash bottle, then record some children's estimates on the board.

- Agree on the best guess with the whole class.

- Demonstrate how to check the estimate with the cup and the squash bottle. Ask the children to record the measure and estimate.

- *How good were our estimates?*

## Plenary

- *Which bottle held more cups of water? Which bottle held more beakers of water?*

- *What do you notice? Why do you think that is?*

- *Which holds more, the beaker or the cup? Why do you think that?*

- Compare the beaker with the cup by filling the larger with the smaller.

- *How many cups of water does the beaker hold?*

# Measures (6)

*Children can compare capacity and to read time to half hours*

| | |
|---|---|
| **Medium-term plan objectives** | • Suggest suitable uniform non-standard, then standard, units and measuring equipment to estimate, then measure, capacity recording estimates and measurements as *'about 3 beakers full'* or *'just under 5 litres'*. |
| | • Solve simple problems involving capacity or time. |
| | • Read time to half an hour on analogue clocks. |
| **Overview** | • Use of uniform units to measure capacity. |
| | • Reading analogue clocks in units of half an hour. |

## How you could plan this unit

| | Stage 1 | Stage 2 | Stage 3 | Stage 4 | Stage 5 |
|---|---|---|---|---|---|
| **Content and vocabulary** | Estimating and measuring using litres<br><br>*measure, compare, guess, estimate, just under/over, full, half full, empty, holds, container, litre* | Solving problems involving capacity | Reading time to the half hour<br><br>*hour, o'clock, half past, clock, hands* | Solving problems involving time<br><br>*time* | |
| **Notes** | Resource pages A and B | Resource page C | Resource page D | Resource page E | |

144

# *Estimating and measuring using litres*

**Advance Organiser**

We are going to measure capacity in litres

**Oral/mental starter p 183**

**You will need:** plastic work tray, litre measure, assortment of plastic bottles filled with water, bucket and plastic tubing, towels and mop, resource pages A and B

## Whole-class work

- Look at the bottles with the children.
- *Which of these do you think holds the most water? Why do you think that?*
- Agree, and record on the board, which has the greatest capacity.
- *How could we find out?*
- Discuss measuring capacity using both comparison and uniform units.
- Introduce the litre measure and write *litre* on a display board.
- *Has anyone seen or heard this word before? Can you say what it means?*
- Discuss that a litre is a *standard measure* of capacity. It is a measure that everyone uses so that everyone can compare different capacities.
- *Now we can use the litre measure to measure the capacity of each bottle. How many litre measures do you think this bottle will fill?*
- Collect some estimates of the first bottle's capacity in litres and record them on the board.

> About 3 litres, just over 3 litres, just less than 3 litres, between 2 litres and 3 litres, nearly 3 litres

- In turn, empty each bottle, carefully pouring first into the litre measure, counting how many litres with the children.
- Compare to their estimates.
- Check the capacity by reversing the process, filling the bottle using the litre measure.
- Repeat for other bottles as necessary.

## Independent, paired or group work

- Ask the children for estimates of how many litres the tray will hold.
- Agree a best guess as a class and write this estimate on an enlarged version of resource page A.
- Fill the tray using the litre measure (starting with the 'waste' water from the earlier emptyings).
- Complete resource page A with the children.
- Ask the children to complete resource page B by colouring or shading the appropriate amount of litre measures to match the capacity of each bottle.

## Plenary

- Choose a pop bottle.
- Discuss how many bottles of pop it would take to fill the tray.
- Draw the correct number of litre measures of water in a line on the whiteboard and ring them in twos or threes to match the capacity of the bottle.
- Ask the children to come to the front and to repeat with other bottles.

**PUPIL PAGE**

Name: _____

# Estimating capacity

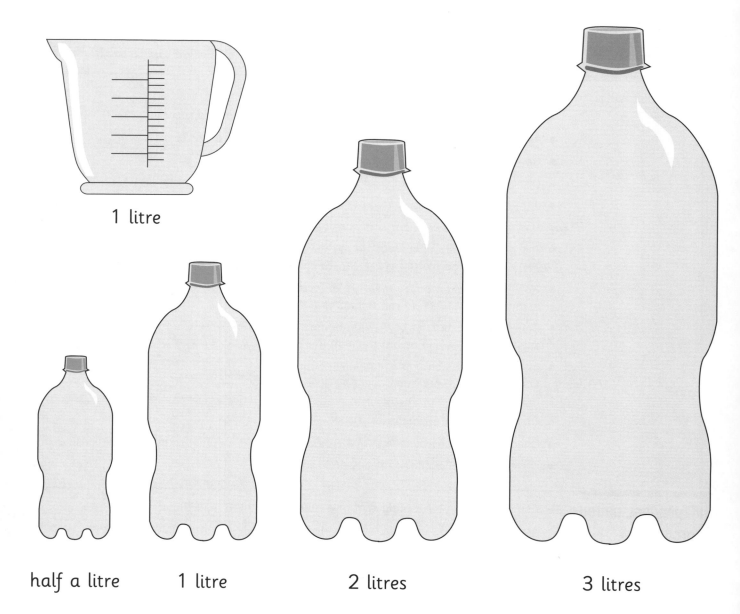

1 litre

half a litre          1 litre          2 litres          3 litres

I estimated the tray could hold ..................... litres.

We measured how much the tray could hold.

The tray holds ..................... litres of water.

**PUPIL PAGE**

Name: _____

# Matching capacity

Shade litre measures to match each capacity.

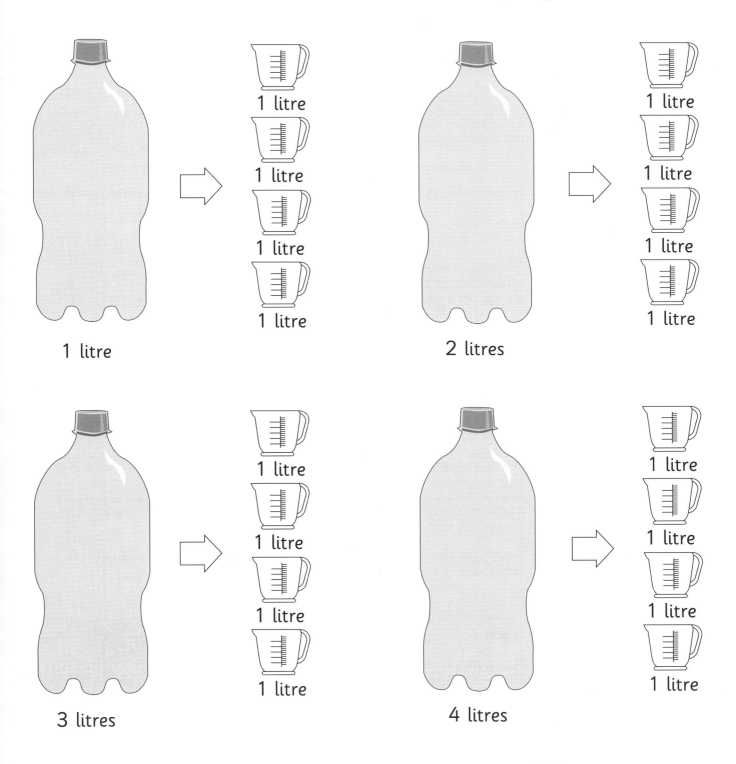

1 litre

2 litres

3 litres

4 litres

*Classworks* © Classworks Numeracy author team, Nelson Thornes Ltd, 2003

# *Solving problems involving capacity*

Oral/mental starter
p 183

**Advance Organiser**

We are going to add two capacities together

**You will need:** plastic pop bottles in 1, 2 and 3 litre sizes, resource page C

## Whole-class work

- Compare the labels on a collection of plastic drink bottles, pointing out the contents given in litres for each.

- With different sized bottles ask: *How many litres of pop would this 2 litre and this 2 litre bottle hold altogether?*

- Ask the children for different ideas.

- *How did you decide that? How can we find out? Do we have to measure?*

- Draw out from the children that we can solve this problem using addition.

- Draw bottles to illustrate the accompanying addition on the whiteboard.

- Repeat for other similar problems involving addition, asking children how they would solve each problem.

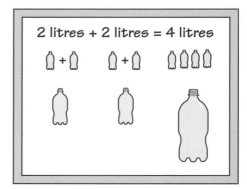

## Independent, paired or group work

- Ask the children to complete resource page C. The last statement is a difficult concept to master.

- In turn, ask groups to go to the 'wet area' and find out if the last statement on the page is correct.

- *Do you think that three 2 litre bottles hold the same as two 3 litre bottles? How can we find out?*

- Ask the children to use the funnel to fill two 3 litre bottles from three 2 litre bottles, or vice versa.

## Plenary

- Look at a few completed activity sheets.

- Demonstrate testing some other capacity additions in the wet area, asking the children to suggest how you can solve each addition and then how to test it.

- *How much water do you think this 1 litre bottle and this 4 litre bottle can hold altogether?*

- *How could you work it out? How can we find out if you are right?*

PUPIL PAGE

Name: _____

# Adding capacities

Shade the bottles on the right to make the total each time.

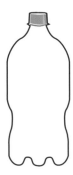

2 litres + 2 litres = 1 litre + 1 litre + 1 litre + 1 litre

1 litre + 1 litre + 1 litre = 3 litres

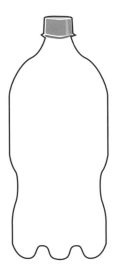

2 litres + 2 litres + 2 litres = 3 litres + 3 litres

# *Reading time to the half hour*

We are going to read the time to the half hour

**Oral/mental starter
p 183**

**You will need:** large analogue clock face (with auto-winding hour hand), resource page D

## Whole-class work

- Use a large clock face with an auto-winding hour hand. Set the clock to 9 o'clock.

- *I am going to move the clock on one hour. What time will it show in one hour?*

- Move the clock on one hour when the children have given some answers.

- *What time does it say now? How do you know? Which is the hour hand? Where is it pointing? Which is the minute hand? Where is it pointing?*

- Repeat a few more one hour moves before positioning the hand to half past the hour.

- *What time does it say now? Where is the hour hand pointing?*

- Draw out from the children that the hand is *halfway past the hour* and that we say that the time is *half past*.

- Move the clock on in half hours, reading off the time each time and pointing out the halfway position of the hour hand.

## Independent, paired or group work

- Ask the children to work on resource page D.

- The first section needs them to write the clock times in numerals.

- The second section requires them to draw hands on the clock face to match the times.

## Plenary

- Let the children set the clock to 'half past' times. *What time does it say?*

- Let them move the clock on in hours and half hours. *What times does it say now?*

- Point out some events which happen at half past the hour.

- Set the clock face to show those times.

- Recite a time rhyme or poem with the class to finish.

( PUPIL PAGE )

Name: _____

# Reading time

This clock says

.............. o'clock.

This clock says

half past ..............

This clock says

.............. o'clock.

This clock says half past ..............

Half past 6

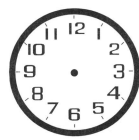

Half past 10

Half past 12

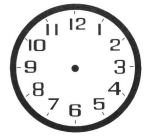

Half past 4

Half past 5

*Classworks* © Classworks Numeracy author team, Nelson Thornes Ltd, 2003

# *Solving problems involving time*

Oral/mental starter
p 183

**Advance Organiser**

We are going to find out what o'clock it will be in one hour

**You will need:** geared clock face, resource page E

## Whole-class work

- Set the clock to read 4 o'clock.

- *What time does this say? How do you know?*

- Ask the children what time it will be in one hour's time.

- *Who can tell me the time one hour later? How can we work that out? How did you know that?*

- Write the children's suggestions on the board, drawing the time as well as writing it each time.

4 o'clock    In 1 hour it will be 5 o'clock

- *One hour from 4 o'clock is 5 o'clock. Four o'clock and one more hour makes 5 o'clock.*

- Repeat for half past 6, and other o'clock and half past times.

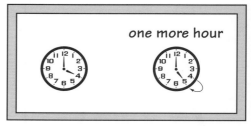

one more hour

## Independent, paired or group work

- Ask the children to complete resource page E.

- They need to write the time on the first clock face, then work out what one hour later will be, and write the time and draw the hands.

## Plenary

- Look at some examples of the children's work and discuss them.

- Draw an o'clock time on the board and write the time in words.

- *What will the time be in two hours?*

- *How did you decide that? How can we work it out?*

- Some children find it easier to draw the clock face and hands, whereas others will work with the numerals, doing an addition.

- Repeat for other times.

Name: _____

# What will the time be?

This clock says ............

1 hour later

This clock says ............

1 hour later

This clock says ............

1 hour later

This clock says ............

1 hour later

This clock says ............

1 hour later

This clock says ............

2 hours later

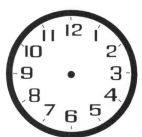

# Shape and Space (1)

**Outcome**

*Children can identify shapes and describe them*

| | |
|---|---|
| **Medium-term plan objectives** | • Use everyday language to describe features of familiar 2-D and 3-D shapes, referring to shapes with flat faces. |
| | • Make and describe models, patterns and pictures using construction kits. |
| | • Recognise simple patterns. |
| | • Use one or more shapes to make repeating patterns. |
| | • Use everyday language to describe position. |
| **Overview** | • Name and describe common two-dimensional shapes. |
| | • Name and describe common three-dimensional shapes. |
| | • Use knowledge of patterns and shapes to solve puzzles. |

## How you could plan this unit

| | Stage 1 | Stage 2 | Stage 3 | Stage 4 | Stage 5 |
|---|---|---|---|---|---|
| **Content and vocabulary** | Name and describe two-dimensional shapes<br><br>*flat, curved, straight, round, corner, point, front, side edge, end, circle, triangle, square, rectangle, star* | Name and describe three-dimensional shapes<br><br>*hollow, solid, cube, cuboid, pyramid, sphere, cone, cylinder* | Use shapes to make patterns and solve problems<br><br>*symmetrical, pattern, repeating pattern, match* | Use everyday language of position | |
| **Notes** | | | | Talk about the patterns from the previous work, using language as above. Children can try to describe a pattern that their partner can copy. | |

# *Name and describe two-dimensional shapes*

**Advance Organiser**

We are going to learn the names of flat shapes

**Oral/mental starter pp 183–184**

**You will need:** a box of shapes (to include as appropriate: circle, semi-circle, triangle, square, rectangle, pentagon, hexagon), logiblocs or other sets of 2-D shapes, cloth bag for paired work, shape stencils for independent work

**Whole-class work**

- Hold up a square. *What is this shape called? Tell me about it.*
- Encourage several descriptions; for example, it has four sides, it has four corners, all the sides are the same length, all the corners are the same size.
- Hold up a rectangle. Ask the children how we tell the difference between a rectangle and a square.
- Look around the classroom for shapes that are squares or rectangles.
- *What shape is the board? What shape is the window?*
- Hold up a triangle. *What is this called? Tell me about it.*
- Draw some different triangles on the board.
- *What are these called? How can you be sure?*
- Establish that every shape with three sides is called a triangle.
- Hold up a circle. *What is this called? How do you know? Are all round shapes called circles?*
- Draw an oval on the board. *Is this a circle? How do you know?*
- Establish that a circle is a round shape that looks the same however you turn it.
- Hold up a hexagon. Count the sides. If children do not know the name, explain that it is called a hexagon.
- Extend this activity as appropriate to your class, or split it across different days.
- Hold up the pentagon and the hexagon. *How can we tell which is which?*
- Revise the shape names by counting down from six: *Which shape has six sides? Five sides? Four sides? What else has four sides? Three sides? One side?*
- *Can anyone think of a shape with two sides?*
- Draw two straight lines on the board to show that they do not join up.
- Show the semi-circle and tell the children its name.

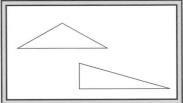

**Independent, paired or group work**

- Put six to ten shapes in the cloth bag.
- Ask pairs of children to take turns to feel in the bag for a shape and name it.
- They should take it out to check that they are right.
- *How did you know it was a square?*

**Plenary**

- Give the children a clue to a shape; for example, *I have four sides all the same length. What am I?*
- When a child names the shape, that child gives the next clue and names the child who should answer.

# Name and describe three-dimensional shapes

**Advance Organiser**

We are going to learn the names of solid shapes

**You will need:** tins, packets, balls and containers, tubes and some boxes without lids, poleidoblocs or similar, cartons and tubes

## Whole-class work

- Sit in a circle on the carpet with the packets and tins in the middle.
- Ask a child to choose any tin or packet and tell you one thing about it.
- Repeat what the child says so that the class can hear.
- A point unrelated to shape, such as *it is a cornflakes packet*, can be an acceptable starting point.
- Ask the child to pass the object to the next person, who also says one thing about it.
- Repeat the two facts about the shape.
- Continue passing the shape on, getting more information from each child.
- As it gets harder to think of more to say, you may need to prompt by saying: *What can you say about the shape of the side/top/bottom of the box?*
- When you have lots of information, reiterate what the children have said.
- *What is the name of the shape of this box/packet/tin?*
- Repeat the name of the shape and say how you know.
- *We know it's a cylinder because, as Tom said, it has a circle at each end. And as Jobeda said, it has a curved face.*
- Show which parts of the shape are 'edges' and which are 'faces'.
- Repeat for other shapes.
- Finish by checking that the children can recognise and name a cylinder, cube, cuboid and sphere.

## Independent, paired or group work

- Give the children a supply of cartons and tubes and some glue or masking tape.
- Ask them to choose three shapes each and decide what to make.
- *Try different arrangements of your shape before fixing it. Draw and name your model.*

## Plenary

- Ask the children who have made models from three boxes to show them to the class.
- Ask each child to name someone in the class.
- That child has to say what shapes they can see in the model.
- Include three- and two-dimensional shape names.
- Praise the children for noticing shapes of faces and shapes in designs on the packets.

# *Use shapes to make patterns and solve problems*

**Advance Organiser**

We are going to use shapes to make patterns and solve some problems

**Oral/mental starter pp 183–184**

**You will need:** 2-D shape tiles, Blu-Tack or tape, necklace (made from a sequence of shaped beads of the same colour on a string), squared paper

## Whole-class work

- Look at the 'necklace' and ask if anyone can tell you what bead comes next.

- Say all the shape names for the beads in sequence together as you check.

- Fix shape tiles to match the sequence on the board.

- *What will come next? How do you know?*

- Ask a child to add the next three tiles in the sequence.

- Agree the correct answer and say the pattern together.

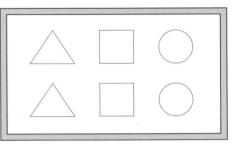

- Ask a child to use four tiles to begin a new pattern.

- That child says, 'Who will put up the next four tiles?' Check the pattern.

- Put up a line of shapes that has no patterned sequence; for example, triangle, square, hexagon, triangle, hexagon, rectangle, triangle.

- *Is this a pattern? What will come next?*

- Make sure that the children understand that a sequence is only a pattern if you can say what will come next.

- Ask the children to change your random sequence so that it is a pattern.

## Independent, paired or group work

- Ask the children to use squared paper to draw their own patterns.

- They should use two different shapes to make the pattern.

- They can draw up to three different patterns.

## Plenary

- Ask different children to hold up their shape patterns.

- Read the sequences to the class yourself; for example, *square, triangle, rectangle, square, triangle, rectangle, square, triangle* ........

- This allows the children to hear, as well as see, the repetition.

- *What shape will come next in this pattern? How do you know? How would you explain the pattern?*

# Shape and Space (2)

**Outcome**

*Children will be able to talk about shapes and use the language of position to solve problems*

## Medium-term plan objectives

- Use everyday language to describe features of familiar 2-D and 3-D shapes, referring to shapes with flat faces, number of faces or corners, number of sides.
- Make and describe models, patterns and pictures using everyday materials, e.g. plasticine.
- Use everyday language to describe position and direction.
- Talk about things that turn.
- Use one or more shapes to make patterns, describe repeating patterns. Predict from simple patterns, and suggest extensions.

## Overview of lessons

- Identify shapes by numbers of faces, edges, corners and sides.
- Make patterns, make predictions and consider 'what happens if...?'.
- Things that turn; use everyday language to describe position and direction.
- Make and describe pictures.

## How you could plan this unit

| | Stage 1 | Stage 2 | Stage 3 | Stage 4 | Stage 5 |
|---|---|---|---|---|---|
| **Content and vocabulary** | Sides and corners<br><br>*shape, flat, curved, straight, round, corner, point, pointed, side* | Edges and faces<br><br>*solid, face, side, edge, end* | Making and completing shape sequences<br><br>*make, build, draw, pattern* | Things that turn<br><br>*position, over, under, underneath, above, below, top, bottom, side, on, in, outside, inside, in front, behind, front, back, beside, next to, opposite, between, middle, edge, left, right, up, down, forwards, backwards, sideways* | Making and describing pictures |
| **Notes** | | Resource page A | Resource page B | Resource page C | Children use 3-D shapes, or draw 2-D shapes, to make a composite picture. They describe their picture to a friend who has to try to draw it as described. Compare and discuss why there are differences. |

# *Sides and corners*

**Advance Organiser**

We are going to find lots of ways to describe flat shapes

**Oral/mental starter**
**pp 183–184**

**You will need:** sets of 2-D shapes

## Whole-class work

- Draw a 'Lost' poster on the board.

- Draw a shape but do not name it.

- Ask the children to tell you a fact about the shape.

- With the children's help, make a list of descriptive features under the shape.

- Discuss and agree each feature as it is suggested.

- Repeat for other shapes as necessary.

- Draw a chart like the one below.

- Ask the children to help you fill in the details for flat shapes.

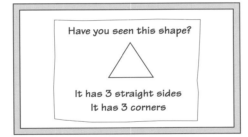

| shape | Straight sides | Curved sides | Corners |
|---|---|---|---|
| circle | | | |
| semi-circle | | | |
| triangle | | | |
| rectangle | | | |
| square | | | |
| pentagon | | | |
| hexagon | | | |

## Independent, paired or group work

- Ask the children to make their own 'Lost' poster for a 2-D shape.

- They should first choose a shape, then draw around it, and finally write two or three sentences about it.

## Plenary

- Ask the children to read the sentences from their posters without showing the picture.

- Other children have to guess the shape's name.

# *Edges and faces*

**Advance Organiser**

We are going to find lots of ways to describe solid shapes

**Oral/mental starter pp 183–184**

**You will need:** sets of 3-D shapes, resource page A (enlarged), a cube made from the net on resource page A, Blu-Tack

## Whole-class work

- Show the children the paper cube.

- *Look at the faces. Help me to count the faces.*

- Choose another 3-D shape. Count the faces with the class again.

- Point out the edges on a cube. Count them carefully.

- *How many edges are there on a cuboid?*

- Count them to check.

- Count the corners on a cube.

- *How many corners on a sphere? How do you know?*

- Draw a 'Lost' poster on the board.

- Stick a 3-D shape onto the top of the poster.

- Ask the children to tell you a fact about the shape.

- With the children's help, make a list of descriptive features under the shape.

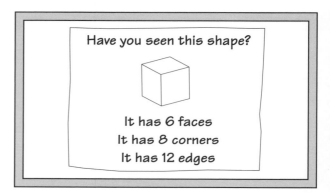

Have you seen this shape?

It has 6 faces
It has 8 corners
It has 12 edges

- Discuss and agree each feature as it is suggested.

- Repeat for other shapes as necessary.

- Look at the chart made from resource page A.

- Ask the children to help you fill in the details for solid shapes.

## Independent, paired or group work

- Ask the children to make their own 'Lost' poster for a 3-D shape.

- They should first choose a shape and then write two or three sentences about it.

## Plenary

- Ask the children to read the sentences from their posters without showing the picture.

- Other children have to guess the shape's name.

**PUPIL PAGE**

Name: _____

# Edges and faces

| Shape | Faces | Straight edges | Curved edges | Corners |
|---|---|---|---|---|
| cylinder | | | | |
| cube | | | | |
| cuboid | | | | |
| sphere | | | | |
| prism | | | | |
| pyramid | | | | |
| cone | | | | |

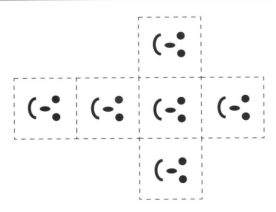

# *Making and completing shape sequences*

**Oral/mental starter pp 183–184**

**Advance Organiser**

We are going to solve some shape puzzles

**You will need:** resource page B (one enlarged and one per child), squared paper

## Whole class work

- Ask six children to come to the front and model a sequence that you whisper to them.

- For example, *one crouching, one standing* all along the line.

- Each time ask another child to come and be the next person in the sequence.

- When six children are in the line, ask them to call out 'crouching', 'standing', 'crouching', 'standing' in turn to reinforce the sequence.

- Ask someone to explain the sequence in their own words.

- *How do you know how the sequence should continue?*

- Look at the enlarged copy of resource page B.

- Talk through the patterns, saying *square, circle, square, circle* and so on.

- Ask different children to explain each pattern and say what is missing.

- Ask the children to draw in the missing shapes for each pattern.

- *How did you decide that? How did you know? Could the pattern be different?*

## Independent, paired or group work

- Give each child a copy of resource page B.

- Ask them to draw the missing shapes.

- Choose two colours for each pattern.

- *How will you colour the shapes and still keep a pattern?*

- Encourage the children to think about the pattern before they begin to use colours.

## Plenary

- Ask the children to talk about the patterns they have coloured or drawn.

- Ask some to 'read out' their patterns. Can the other children draw them to match?

- Check that they still make a repeating pattern.

- *Why does colouring the shapes make it harder? What did you have to remember?*

- For children who used squared paper, why were some patterns in lines and others alternate?

**PUPIL PAGE**

Name: _____

# Shape sequences

What comes next?

Fill the gaps.

What comes next?

Fill the gaps.

Fill the gaps.

What do you get if you draw this pattern using triangles?

# Things that turn

**Advance Organiser**

We are going to learn words that help us explain where things are and how they move

**Oral/mental starter
pp 183–184**

**You will need:** resource page C cut into cards, a soft toy, objects that turn (such as a jar with a lid, the hands on a clock, and so on)

## Whole class work

- Talk about things that can turn. Have some to show the children.

- Make a list on the board from the children's suggestions.

- Mime different turning actions. Can the children guess what is turning?

- Revise 'right' and 'left' by saying: *put up your right hand; touch your left knee; show me your left thumb; face to your right; point to your right ear* and so on.

> steering wheel, handlebars, hands on a clock, lid on a jar, a screwdriver, a playground roundabout, a revolving door, a door handle, a wheel

- Ask the children to sit in a circle on the carpet.

- Place a soft toy in the middle. Label the toy's right and left arms with sticky labels.

- Cut up the cards from resource page C and place them in a pile face down.

- Take turns around the circle to pick up a card, read the words aloud and move the toy.

- Make sure that everyone agrees. Put the card back at the bottom of the pack.

- When the cards have all been used, shuffle them and continue. Make sure that everyone has a turn.

## Independent, paired or group work

- Use a box of 3-D shapes or bricks such as poleidoblocs.

- Ask each child to choose four shapes and make them into a model.

- Ask each child to describe their model using the names of the shapes and the positions in relation to each other; for example, *I have a cone on top of a cube. There is a small cube on each side.*

## Plenary

- Ask one child to come to the front.

- Ask another child to give them a direction, as for the toy, such as *Turn and face left, Turn around once* and so on.

- Use the cards again if you need to.

- After obeying three directions the child chooses another child to come to the front.

# Direction cards

| | |
|---|---|
| Turn and face left. | Turn and face right. |
| Move sideways one pace. | Turn all the way around once. |
| Move backwards one pace. | Face the opposite way. |
| Move forwards one pace. | Move forwards one pace. |
| Move across the circle. | Sit next to a girl. |
| Sit between two boys. | Sit in the centre of the circle. |

*Classworks* © Classworks Numeracy author team, Nelson Thornes Ltd, 2003

# Shape and Space (3)

**Outcome**

*Children will be able to talk about, and recognise, shapes and use them to make patterns*

**Medium-term plan objectives**

- Fold shapes in half, then make them into symmetrical patterns.
- Begin to relate solid shapes to pictures of them.
- Use one or more shapes to make, describe and continue repeating patterns.
- Make whole turns and half turns.
- Use everyday language to describe position, direction and movement.
- Investigate general statements about shapes.

**Overview**

- Relate solid shapes to pictures of them.
- Use half turns to make repeating patterns.
- Fold shapes in half, then make them into symmetrical patterns.
- Investigate general statements about shapes.

## How you could plan this unit

| | Stage 1 | Stage 2 | Stage 3 | Stage 4 | Stage 5 |
|---|---|---|---|---|---|
| **Content and vocabulary** | Pictures of solid shapes<br><br>*cube, cuboid, pyramid, sphere, cone, cylinder* | Using half turns to make repeating patterns<br><br>*pattern, shape, turn, whole turn, half turn* | Folding shapes to make symmetrical patterns<br><br>*symmetrical, repeating pattern, match* | Investigate general statements about shapes<br><br>*curved, straight, corner, point, pointed, side* | |
| **Notes** | Resource page A | | | | |

# Pictures of solid shapes

**Advance Organiser**

We are going to look at solid shapes and match them to their pictures

Oral/mental starter
pp 183–184

**You will need:** sets of 3-D shapes, bricks or a variety of empty tins and boxes, resource page A (enlarged), paper

## Whole-class work

- Allow the children to look at the boxes or shapes from different angles.

- Talk about what shapes they can see from different positions.

- Point out how the circle on top of a cylinder seems to change shape as you move it.

- *We know that this shape is really a circle, but from this position it looks like an oval.*

- Draw an oval and two sides of a cylinder. Join the lines across the bottom.

- Hold the shape at the same angle next to the drawing, matching the drawing to the shape.

- Turn the cylinder on its side and draw it again in this position.

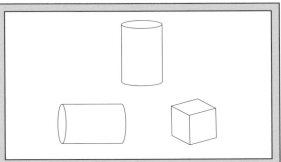

- Repeat with other shapes. When you look at a cube, notice that the side and top of the cube no longer look square, although they are.

- *Does any shape look the same whichever why you turn it?*

- Give out all the cards from resource page A, one to each child.

- Duplicate the shape cards to involve all the children.

- The children have to decide how to group them into sets of matching names and shapes.

## Independent, paired or group work

- Ask each child to choose a 3-D shape.

- They should take the shape and draw it twice: once from above, once from the side.

- *Draw what you can see from each position, not what you think is there.*

- They can repeat with other 3-D shapes.

- Help the children to draw what they see from each position and relate that to the solid shape.

## Plenary

- Look at the children's drawings of the shapes.

- Ask them to try to name each other's shapes from the two viewpoints.

( CUT-OUT )

# Shape cards

| | | |
|---|---|---|
| cylinder | cuboid | cube |
| sphere | prism | cone |

# Using half turns to make repeating patterns

**Advance Organiser**

We are going to turn shapes to make repeating patterns

**You will need:** 2-D shape tiles, squared paper

## Whole-class work

- Have a brief session with everyone doing whole and half turns on a rug.

- Establish that a whole turn means *all the way around* and a half turn means *half way around*.

- Draw a triangle on the board. Draw another one upside down beside it.

- *What is the same about the two shapes? What is different about the two shapes?*

- *What have I done to the second triangle?*

- Establish that you have turned it around so that it is upside down or have made a half turn.

- Draw another two triangles to make a pattern.

- *What comes next?*

- Ask three or four children to draw the next triangle, keeping the same pattern going.

- Call out the pattern with the class by describing the shapes; for example, right way up, upside down, right way up, and so on.

- Repeat with other shapes.

## Independent, paired or group work

- Ask some groups to use squared paper to draw shapes in a repeating pattern by turning the shapes a half turn up and down or right and left.

- Other groups can be given a set of 2-D shape tiles.

- They can arrange these into alternating patterns.

## Plenary

- Ask four children to make themselves into a 'facing' left', 'facing right' pattern.

- Get other children to join the line.

- *Which way should you face?* Check the sequence together.

- Ask four children to make a different pattern: get the children to put their right hand up, then ask the second and fourth children to turn half way round.

- Select volunteers to add to the pattern.

- Check that each child is facing the correct way and has their right hand up.

# Folding shapes to make symmetrical patterns

**Advance Organiser**

We are going to fold shapes and make symmetrical patterns

Oral/mental starter
pp 183–184

**You will need:** tracing paper A4 size, painting paper cut into circles, rectangles, squares, isosceles triangles, paints, set of dominoes

## Whole-class work

- Show the children a set of double dominoes.

- *What can you say about these dominoes?*

- Draw out from the children that both the number and the pattern is the same on each side.

- Sort the doubles one at a time into symmetrical and non-symmetrical sets.

- *What do you notice about this group of doubles?*

- Draw out or explain that these dominoes are symmetrical, because the halves match exactly.

- Look at the non-doubles and notice that the number is different and the pattern is different.

- *These ones are not symmetrical.*

- Fold a piece of paper in half and paint two spots on one side in a domino pattern.

- Fold the paper while the paint is still wet.

- *What pattern will I make?*

- Repeat for a symmetrical double 2 pattern.

- Talk about the differences. Repeat with three spots.

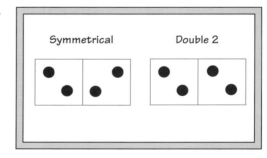

## Independent, paired or group work

- Use the ready-cut shaped painting paper.

- Ask each child to choose a shape and fold it in half.

- Help them to match the edges carefully. Make a firm crease.

- Show the children how to paint a pattern on one half of the shape, then fold it and press so that the paint colours the other half before it dries.

- Display all the symmetrical patterns.

## Plenary

- Look at some of the paintings.

- Help the children to find colours on one half and look for the matching colour on the other half.

- *Does the painting remind you of anything? Are the faces symmetrical?*

- *Where would the fold go? What else is symmetrical? A butterfly? A tree?*

# *Investigate general statements about shapes*

**Advance Organiser**

We are going to think of some rules about shapes, then check to see if they are always true

**Oral/mental starter pp 183–184**

**You will need:** drinking straws cut to various lengths

---

**Whole-class work**

- Sit in a circle on the carpet.
- *What do we know about triangles?*
- Write the definitions on the board as they are suggested.
- Give each child three drinking straws at random.
- Some will have three the same length, some will have two the same, some will have all three different.
- Ask them to use their straws to make a triangle.
- *Try rearranging the straws. Can you make your triangle look different?*
- Move some varied triangles to the middle of the space.
- *Are they all triangles? How do we know?*
- *Is our rule true, that triangles have three sides and three corners?*
- Ask the children to tell you a rule about squares.
- Use four straws the same length.
- Ask one child to make a square with the straws.
- Move the straws to change the angles.
- *Is this a square? Are there four sides? Are all the sides the same length?*
- *How can we change our rule?*
- Arrive at a rule that says that all the corners must be the same, or four 'square' corners, or four right angles.

> They have three straight sides
> They have three corners

> Is this a triangle?
> It has three sides ...
>
> Is this a triangle?
> There are three corners ...

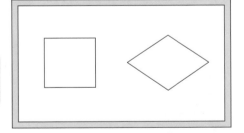

---

**Independent, paired or group work**

- Ask the children to use all the straws of different lengths.
- Get them to investigate the shapes that can be made with four sides.
- *Are they all the same? Which ones can you name?*
- Ask them to think of a rule to describe a rectangle and check that it is always true.

---

**Plenary**

- Ask the children to draw named shapes on the board; for example, triangle, square, rectangle, hexagon.
- After each shape has been drawn, check it and repeat its definition with the class: *Does it have six sides? Does it have six corners? Are the sides straight? So is it a hexagon?*

---

# *Handling Data (1)*

**Outcome**

*Children will be able to talk about finding out their favourite*

| | |
|---|---|
| **Medium-term plan objectives** | • Solve a problem by sorting information using objects or pictures. |
| **Overview** | • Carry out a simple investigation and record the results in tables. |

## How you could plan this unit

| | Stage 1 | Stage 2 | Stage 3 | Stage 4 | Stage 5 |
|---|---|---|---|---|---|
| **Content and vocabulary** | Favourite colours<br><br>*count, sort, vote, group, set, list, table* | Favourite pets | | | |
| **Notes** | | | | | |

172

# Favourite colours

**Oral/mental starter pp 183–184**

**You will need:** examples of pictograms, 2 cm-squared paper, large collection of linking cubes

## Whole-class work

- Ask individual children to say what is their favourite colour.
- *How can we find out the favourite colour of everyone in the class?*
- Draw out, if it is not suggested, the idea of a table, graph or chart.
- Show the children examples of pictograms.
- *Does anyone know what this is? Can anyone tell me what it is for?*
- Establish that we can use objects or pictures to show information.
- *We are going to find out our favourite colour of cube.*
- Ask all the children to give you a cube of their favourite colour from those on the table.
- Suggest different ways of comparing the numbers and draw out that columns or rows of cubes that make for easy comparison.
- Establish the importance of a base line and that each square is the same size.
- Build up a physical graph using columns of the same colour of cube.
- *Who can tell me which is our favourite colour of cube?*
- *How did you know?*

## Independent, paired or group work

- Ask the children to work in groups of three or four to find the group's favourite colour of cube from a set limited to three colours in a similar way.
- Draw the class together again.
- *Can we all see which colour is the favourite in each group?*
- *What will happen when the cubes are put back in the box? How will we know which is the favourite then?*
- Draw out the idea of a permanent record.
- Give each child a sheet of 2 cm-squared paper and ask them to write the name of the colours they chose from at the bottom, then colour squares in columns to represent their cube graphs. They should add a title.

## Plenary

- Record the whole-class graph on the board by drawing squares to represent the cubes.
- Compare the heights of the columns.
- *Which was our favourite colour of cube?*
- *Which was the second favourite?*
- *Was there a colour that was no one's favourite?*
- How do we know?
- Count up the cubes in each column.
- *Do we have to count to see which is the favourite?*

# Favourite pets

**Advance Organiser**

We are going to find out what is our favourite animal to have as a pet

**You will need:** squares of coloured paper, large sheets of paper

**Oral/mental starter pp 183–184**

## Whole-class work

- Discuss what each child's favourite animal would be to have as a pet.

- Discuss what their favourite pet would be out of, for example: a tiger, a dragon, a unicorn and a bear.

- Write those names on the board.

- *How can we find out which is the class's favourite?*

- Lead a discussion of ideas.

- Ask the children to come to the board and draw a square above their favourite to form columns.

- *What must we always do when we draw a graph?*

- Help the children to keep their squares the same size – discuss why this is important.

- Establish the importance of the base line on a chart.

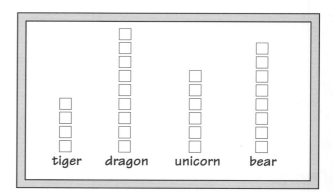

## Independent, paired or group work

- Ask the children in pairs to stick squares of coloured paper onto a large sheet of paper to make a graph.

- They should copy the class results from the board.

- Ensure they discuss how to make sure that the graph is accurate.

## Plenary

- *How can we tell which animal would be our favourite pet?*

- Look at some of the children's sheets.

- Discuss how it is easier or harder to see which is the favourite from different sheets, and why.

- *How else could we find out?*

- Discuss voting, recording numbers or tallies, and so on.

# *Handling Data (2)*

**Outcome**

*Solve problems by sorting information and recoding it using a simple table*

| | |
|---|---|
| **Medium-term plan objectives** | • Solve a problem by sorting, classifying and organising information in a list or simple table. |
| **Overview** | • Making subjective choices and placing data in a simple table.<br><br>• Comparing the results of a simple investigation and placing the data in a simple table. |

## How you could plan this unit

| | Stage 1 | Stage 2 | Stage 3 | Stage 4 | Stage 5 |
|---|---|---|---|---|---|
| **Content and vocabulary** | Sorting animals<br><br>*count, sort, vote, list, group, set, table, how did you work it out?, what could we try next?* | Who can hold the most? | | | |
| **Notes** | | | | | |

# Sorting animals

**Advance Organiser**

We are going to sort out some animals

Oral/mental starter
pp 183–184

**You will need:** A3 paper

## Whole-class work

- Talk about pets and who has got what.

- Talk about more unusual pets if none of the children have them; for example, snakes or spiders.

- *What can you tell me about that sort of pet?*

- Write some of the facts about the pets up on the board.

- *If we had to tell a friend about different sorts of pets, how could we do that?*

- *How could we sort out our pets into groups?*

- Brainstorm ways of categorising pets into a small number of groups.

- *Some pets need a cage, some pets need lots of expensive food, some pets can be kept in the house and some can't.*

- Decide on some categories to sort the pets into and draw the following table.

- *We are going to sort pets into those that can be kept in the house and those that can't.*

- Get ideas for the children and fill in the table.

> dogs have to be walked
>
> cats can go out by themselves
>
> hamsters live in a cage
>
> you have to change a goldfish's water

**Sorting Pets**

| pets we can keep in the house |
| --- |
|  |
| pets we can't keep in the house |
|  |

## Independent, paired or group work

- Now ask children to work in pairs to decide on two new categories to sort the same pets.

- Encourage sensible categories, such as *pets that are kept in a cage and pets that are not kept in a cage,* or *pets that need walking and pets that don't need walking.*

- Encourage each pair to draw a table with headings, and then write in the names of pets.

## Plenary

- Ask each pair to prepare a question, based on their table, to ask the rest of the class.

- For example: *where would a lion go on our table?*

- *What if someone had a pet rat? Which part would that go on?*

- Ask pairs in turn to display their 'sort' and ask their question.

# *Who can hold the most?*

**Advance Organiser**

We are going to see who can hold the most cubes using two hands

**Oral/mental starter pp 183–184**

**You will need:** linking cubes, A3 paper

## Whole-class work

- Put one of your hands into a box of cubes and take a handful, but leave your hand in the box.

- *How many of these cubes do you think I am holding?*

- Count them together with the children.

- *How many cubes do you think you can hold?*

- *How can we find out? How could we record our results?*

- Have a brief discussion of tables.

- Draw the following table with each child's name written on it.

- In turn, each child takes a handful of cubes and counts how many.

- Record how many on the table.

- *Whose hand held the most?*

- *How do you know that?*

- *Whose hand held the least?*

- *Whose hand held the second most?*

| Name | Number of cubes held |
| --- | --- |
|  |  |
|  |  |
|  |  |

## Independent, paired or group work

- In groups, ask the children to collect as many cubes as they can using two hands (held away from the body).

- They should put them down in front of them in their group, being careful not to mix up their cubes with someone else's.

- Ask them to record the scores of each in their group in a table like the one on the board, writing in their names first.

## Plenary

- Look at the scores from each group.

- Record the highest score (and scorer's name) from each group in your table on the board.

- Compare a few of the children's hand sizes.

- Ask each of them to demonstrate how they picked up the cubes.

- Ask a lower scoring child to try to better their own score using the same technique as one of the high scorers.

# Handling Data (3)

**Outcome**

*Solve a problem by organising information in a list or table and discuss and explain the results*

| **Medium-term plan objectives** | • Solve a problem by organising information in a list or table.<br>• Discuss and explain the results. |
|---|---|
| **Overview** | • Collect and collate data, present it and discuss the results. |

## How you could plan this unit

| | Stage 1 | Stage 2 | Stage 3 | Stage 4 | Stage 5 |
|---|---|---|---|---|---|
| **Content and vocabulary** | What's our favourite book?<br><br>*count, sort, vote, list, group, set, table, what could we try next?, how did you work it out?* | Favourite vegetable | | | |
| **Notes** | | | | | |

# What's our favourite book?

**Advance Organiser**

We are going to find out the favourite book of the class

**You will need:** A4 paper

**Oral/mental starter pp 183–184**

## Whole-class work

- Select four of the most popular fiction books from the class library.

- Discuss the merits of each and ask a few children which one they like best.

- *How could we decide which is the favourite book of the whole class?*

- Discuss how they could find out, how you could present the information, and so on.

- Draw a chart on the board and ask children in turn which is their favourite.

- Write the name of each child on the chart.

- *Can we see which is the favourite? Can we see which is the second favourite?*

- *How could we make it easier to see our results?*

**Which is Your Favourite Book?**

| Utterly me, Clarice Bean | Pants |
|---|---|
| Room on the Broom | Click, Clack, Moo |

## Independent, paired or group work

- Ask the children to work together in their groups with a sheet of A4 paper.

- First of all they need to draw a table and write the names of the books in the correct space on their sheet.

- *I would like you to count how many names are in each section on our class chart, and just write the number on your own chart.*

## Plenary

- Look at the table on the board.

- *Which was this group's favourite book?*

- *What can we say about the books and who liked them?*

- *Do only boys like* Pants?

- *Who liked* Room on the Broom?

- Look at some of the children's sheets.

- *What is different about these sheets?*

- *Is it easier or harder to see which book is the favourite?*

- *Why do you think that is?*

- Read the favourite book as a reward.

# *Favourite vegetable*

We are going to find out which is our favourite vegetable

**Oral/mental starter**
pp 183–184

**You will need:** 2 cm-squared paper, name cards for each person in the class (including one for yourself), Blu-Tack, giant sheet (2 x 2 sheets of backing paper) on the wall

## Whole-class work

- Talk about whether children like various vegetables, from a selection of five or six.

- *How can we find out what the class's favourite vegetable is?*

- Discuss various methods, including a show of hands, tally charts and so on.

- Agree that today we will make a chart.

- Choose five or six (perhaps by a show of hands) and make labels for them to place in a spaced out column down the side of a large sheet of paper.

- If appropriate, add a simple drawing to represent the food.

- Place your name card to the right of your choice of favourite vegetable.

- Ask all the children to come to the front to place their name card in the appropriate place, building up rows to make a chart.

- *Which is our favourite? How can you tell?*

- Draw out the idea that because the names are on cards and placed in rows with a base line, we can quickly see which is the favourite without having to count.

## Independent, paired or group work

- Ask the children to colour squares on squared paper to match the chart on the display sheet.

- *Make sure you write the name of each vegetable next to each row.*

- After the children have done this, discuss the display chart.

- *If I wanted to know how many people voted for the favourite, how could I find that out?*

- Ask the children to count up the cards in each row and write the total of each on their charts.

## Plenary

- Discuss the results of the survey.

- *Which is the least favourite vegetable? How can you tell?*

- *Which is the second favourite?*

- This is a difficult idea – if necessary, remove the cards of the favourite vegetable, and say: *Which is the favourite now? How could you tell?*

- Discuss different ways of presenting the same data and different ways of finding out.

- *How could we find out our parents' favourite vegetables? What about the whole school's favourite vegetable?*

# *Oral/mental starter ideas*

## Properties of number

### Counting together

Practise counting as a class in ones, twos or tens, forwards or backwards, changing direction when the last child stops counting or when a target number is reached. See how far you can go each time.

### Change

Begin a count forwards as a class in ones, twos or tens. At a certain point shout *Change* and the class then count backwards in the same amount. Repeat the change several times.

### Counting around

Count around the circle, one child saying a number at a time. Count in ones. After a few goes, stop the count and ask *Who will say three? Count on four more people. How many have we counted?*

### Counting stick

Count with the class on a counting stick labelled in ones or twos or tens. After a few goes, remove a label at random. Repeat the count to see if the children know which number the blank section represents. Remove another label. Repeat until the stick is empty or the children are unable to count.

### Blast off!

Count down around a circle of children from 10 or 20, or in tens from 100 to zero. When you reach zero, all jump up shouting *Blast off!* Start at different places around the circle. Vary whether you are counting back in ones, twos or tens. Vary the starting point. *Who knows the person who will say 1? Who will say a number before we get to Blast off?*

### Labelling

Show the children a blank counting stick. Ask the children in turn to come up and label a number, either ones to 10, twos to 20 and so on. Ask first for 0 and the end of the sequence. The class can help each child to label the stick.

## Addition and subtraction

### Number bonds up to 5

Choose a target number. Going around the circle, each child has to give a pair of number bonds for that number. Reversals are fine but anyone who repeats exactly a pair already used is 'out'.

### Number bonds to 10

Call out a number less than 10 and ask the class to call out its number bond to 10. Call out 10 or 0 at some point. Alternatively, give children a number card to 10 each. They should find a partner to make 10 altogether.

### How many more?

Write a target number up to 10 on the board. Call out a smaller number and ask how many more to make the target number. Change the target number.

### One more, one less

Call out a number and ask for one more or one less from the class. Extend to two more or two less.

### Addition doubles

Call out a number and ask for its addition double. Go around the class, each child saying the addition double of a number starting with 1 + 1, continuing with 1 + 1 = 2, 2 + 2 = 4, 3 + 3 = 6 and so on.

### Halves and doubles

Ask for halves and doubles in different ways. *Double 5. Half of 4. Two sixes. 7 plus 7. How many eyes have three people? How many shoes on eight feet?*

### Tens

Ask questions adding or subtracting 10. Call out numbers and ask for 10 more or 10 less. Show a 1 to 100 grid as support if necessary, pointing down the columns as you ask the questions.

## Solving problems

### Think of a number

Ask simple 'think of a number' questions. *I think of a number and add 2. I get 5. What was my number? I think of a number and take away 1. I get 2. What was my number?*

### Coin totals

Ask some quick coin-totalling questions. *What is 2p and 5p altogether? 10p and 2p? 1p and 20p? 1p and another 1p?* Alternatively, give each child in the circle a coin. Ask two children to stand up. The class add the total of their two coins. Repeat for lots of pairs of children.

### Change from...

Write a coin on the board, such as 10p. Tell the children to imagine they go into a shop with this coin. You are going to call out what they spend and they tell you what change you should get. Go around the circle asking the children in turn.

### How can I make...

Write a target amount of money on the board, such as 7p. Ask the children, in turn, how they could make that amount using coins.

## Measures

### How long until...

Show the children a clock. Ask some quick-time questions in hours. *How long from 2 o'clock till 3 o'clock? Five o'clock till 8 o'clock? It is 9 o'clock. What time was it one hour ago?*

### In order

Ask the children to get into order in a line from the tallest to the shortest. Move the chairs and tables back first!

### Taller than

Choose a classroom item such as a metre stick. Ask the children to stand up in turn. The class decide if they are taller than or shorter than the object, and then test. They get into two groups, appropriately.

### Days, months, seasons

Ask the class to chant the days of the week in order, starting from different days. Repeat for the months and seasons of the year. *What is the next month? Who will say Sunday?*

## Shape and space

### Where am I?

Describe a position in the classroom using prepositions and landmarks; for example, *I have a door to my right and a bookshelf behind me. I am beside a big table with a sink to my left.* Ask a child to stand in the place you describe. After several turns ask a child to describe a place in a similar way.

### Drawing shapes

Ask a child to draw on the board, a shape with a given number of sides or corners; for example, *Draw a shape with three sides.* Ask the child to name the shape. That child then gives similar instructions to the next child.

### Name that shape

Give each child a set of cards with shape names on. Hold up a shape – the children have to hold up the correct card.

### Tell me the shape

Revise the names of 2-D shapes by playing 'Tell me the name'. Begin by saying *Tell me the name of a shape with three corners.* The child who gets the right answer says the next 'Tell me the name...' sentence and chooses who will answer.

### Shape quiz

Ask the children to tell you the shape of the object you say; for example, *A tin of beans – what shape is it? A football? A table top? A hoop? A cereal packet? A die?* Ask the children to think of real objects and ask others to name the shape.

### Show me a shape

Use a box of 3-D shapes or blocks such as Poleidoblocs. Say to different children: *Show me a circle, Show me a cuboid, Show me a rectangle* and so on. Show the class, making sure that they understand when a whole shape is being shown (for example, cuboid) and when it is one surface (for example, rectangle).

### Clapping patterns

Revise the idea of sequential patterns using clapping games. Ask the children to join in; for example, clap hands twice then knees twice and repeat, saying *hands, hands, knees, knees* to reinforce the pattern as they do so. Change to tapping head once then shoulders twice, repeat. Ask a child to model a simple sequence for everyone to repeat.

### 'Simon says' positions

Play 'Simon says' using prepositions. Remind the children that they only move if 'Simon says'. Use a series of commands; for example, *Simon says put your hands behind your back. Simon says put your hand under your chin. Simon says look up/down, put a finger next to your nose/between your teeth*. Use a variety of prepositions. Children who move when Simon didn't say so are 'out'.

### Familiar shapes

Ask the children to tell you the name of the shape when you say the name of an object; for example, a tin of soup, a stock cube, a cornflakes packet, a marble, the roof of a house, a toilet roll, a tissue box, a magic marker, a new eraser, a dice, a Cornetto, a domino. Ask the children to add some more things that are also 3-D shapes.

### What's the opposite?

Have a quick quiz where you say a word and the children say the opposite; for example, up/down, in/out, right/left, under/over, high/low, inside/outside, top/bottom, in front/behind, forwards/backwards, towards/away from, front/back.

### Folding in half

Use some clothes from the cloakroom or from lost Property. Explain that you are going to fold things in half. Ask someone to fold a scarf in half. *What do you notice about the two halves?* Do the same with a T-shirt, a jacket, a pair of shorts. Talk about the symmetrical halves. *What happens if you fold it the other way? Are the halves symmetrical?* Ask the children to explain what 'symmetrical' means.

### Find a shape with...

Use a box of flat shapes. Ask the children to come and find shapes that match a description; for example, *Come and get a shape with three corners.* If a child can name it, they can hold the shape. If not, it goes back in the box. That child says the next description and names the person to get it. Have enough turns to use a variety of descriptions of the most common shapes.

## Handling data

### To the vote

Write a choice on the board; for example, *Which are best, dogs or cats?* Ask the children to vote with a show of hands and count up the votes. If possible, take a vote on something the class can really decide – whether to play a certain game or another at playtime, or whether to read a certain favourite book or another.

### Lists

Organise a list of names of children in the class that have more than four letters. Ask the children in turn to say their name and how many letters. Write the list on the board.

### Who holds the most?

Ask the children in turn to take a handful of cubes or counters. Count how many and write the total on the board. Repeat for the class, building up a list on the board. *Who holds the most?*